Do It Yourself
Pure Plant
Skin Care

Do It Yourself
Pure Plant
Skin Care

Carolyn Stubbin

Published by
The International Centre of Holistic Aromatherapy

First published in Australia 1999 by
The International Centre of Holistic Aromatherapy
PO Box 273, Zillmere Q 4034

Desktop publishing by Page People Pty Ltd (www.pagepeople.com.au), Noosa, Queensland

Printed in Australia by Watson Ferguson and Co., Brisbane

National Library of Australia Cataloguing Publication Data
Stubbin, Carolyn.
      Do it yourself pure plant skin care

      1st ed.
      Includes index.
      ISBN 0 646 38318 3

      1. Herbal cosmetics. 2. Cosmetics. 3. Aromatherapy.
      4. Beauty, Personal. I. Battaglia, Salvatore. II. Title

      668.55

Acknowledgements

There are many people I would like to thank for their encouragement, support and inspiration. Especially my husband, Salvatore Battaglia, and my parents, Beverly and Robert Stubbin, for their support in my journey through life and in my pursuit of knowledge in natural therapies.

Thank you to all my students and customers who have been a constant source of information and questions which inspire me to attain ever more knowledge. Keep asking and keep telling me of your successes too.

I am also indebted to all the herbalists and aromatherapists who have gone before me. The knowledge you have imparted has been truly invaluable.

About the author

Carolyn Stubbin was born in 1967 in Boonah, a country town in south-east Queensland where she grew up and lived with her family on a farm. From a very young age, Carolyn knew she wanted to be a herbalist and work with plant medicines. Carolyn is a qualified herbalist, aromatherapist and beauty therapist with further qualifications in natural therapies and acupuncture.

Carolyn and her partner Salvatore Battaglia founded The Perfect Potion and have developed a range of pure aromatherapy products. Carolyn conducts workshops in making your own pure plant skin care products. She is a member of the National Herbalists Association of Australia.

Foreword

This book is for those of you who love to use nothing but the best, the purest and the finest quality plant preparations on your body. You will learn how to make luxurious moisturising creams, exotic soaps, relaxing bath soaks, healing ointments and more, using the purest plant and natural ingredients.

The ingredients recommended in this book have been chosen both for their therapeutic properties as well as their availability. Do not limit your preparations to the ingredients recommended in this book. You may find that your knowledge of your local wild plants and herbs or having access to rarer ingredients will allow you to substitute them in many of the recipes. Once you have mastered the basics, the possibilities are infinite.

As well as containing pure plant ingredients your preparations will contain lots of love - a truly special ingredient. I wish you joy in making your own preparations from this book.

Please Note

All ingredients must be selected and used with care and respect to ensure compatibility with your skin. The best quality ingredients available should always be selected.

The recipes given in this book are not to be used as substitutes for professional health or medical advice.

The author and the publisher, therefore, cannot accept any responsibility for any mishap resulting from the use of any ingredient, recipe or method described in this book.

Contents

INTRODUCTION

- Basics
- Raw Ingredients
- Aromatherapy
- Herbal Preparations
- Ointments and Balms
- Gels
- Emulsions

Basics

Equipment and Utensils

To make your wonderful pure plant preparations you will require a variety of basic equipment and utensils. Most of the utensils you need can be found in your kitchen. If not, you should be able to readily obtain them from kitchen shops, supermarkets, department stores or hardware stores. The list below summarises the range of utensils that you may need to utilise.

Equipment and Utensils

- Scales — kitchen diet scales or electronic scales
- Cooking thermometers — two are usually required
- Heat resistant glass mixing bowls
- Mixing bowls — plastic, stainless steel, ceramic or glass
- Measuring spoons
- Stainless steel teaspoon
- Stainless steel tablespoon
- Wooden or plastic mixing spoon
- Spatula
- Measuring cups
- Measuring jugs
- Sharp knife

- Stainless steel saucepans
- Frypan
- Cutting board
- Strainer/sieve
- Teapot
- Kettle
- Funnel
- Cheesecloth/muslin
- Coffee filter paper
- Grater
- Egg whisk
- Electric hand mixer
- Mortar and pestle
- Electric coffee grinder
- Rubber gloves
- Oven gloves
- Blanket
- Milk cartons
- Candle moulds
- Chocolate moulds

- Plastic food containers
- Pipettes, eye droppers
- Glass jars
- Glass bottles
- Plastic bottles
- Muffin tins
- Spray bottles
- Pump bottles
- Labels
- Marking pens
- Notebook
- Scissors
- Calculator

Hygiene and Sterilisation

It is important to consider hygiene and sterilisation for two reasons. Firstly, disregard for hygiene and sterilisation will ensure your beautiful preparations will deteriorate quickly and secondly, the application of preparations containing bacteria and mould may be harmful, especially if applied to broken or weakened skin.

Therefore, the following points need to be addressed when making your preparations.

- Wash your hands.
- Make sure the utensils you use are clean.
- Ensure that your containers are clean and have been sterilised if you intend storing your preparations for any length of time.

Sterilising Containers

- Glass jars and bottles can be sterilised by boiling them for 20 minutes then leaving them to dry completely, away from pollution or contaminants. A solution used to sterilise babies' bottles is a useful alternative.

- Plastic jars and bottles and lids can be sterilised in a solution which is used to sterilise babies' bottles.

- When removing your preparations from their container, use a clean spoon or spatula rather than your fingers which are naturally covered in bacteria and other contaminants.

Allergic Reactions

Many people are under the impression that natural ingredients will not cause adverse reactions. While they are less likely to, there is no guarantee that it may not happen. Some people are simply more prone to allergic reactions than others.

Immediately wash the substance from your skin if an allergic reaction occurs.

Sometimes it may take several applications of a preparation before a reaction occurs. If the reaction appears to be due to your preparation it is easier to identify the allergen. Perform a patch test by applying one of the ingredients to a band-aid and attaching it firmly to the soft skin just inside your elbow. Leave it on for 24 hours and check for any reaction. You may want to test two substances on each elbow at the same time. Just make sure they are far enough away from each other to be able to distinguish between each substance.

Remember that pure essential oils are very concentrated substances and that lowering the concentration used in your prepartion may be helpful if a reaction occurs.

Sometimes stress, heat, cold, change in humidity, change in diet, illness or medication can make you more prone to an allergic reaction than you otherwise might be. If you are unable to identify the allergen in your preparation, the allergen may be some other agent with which you have come into contact, such as an animal, plant or cleaning agent.

Raw Ingredients

Fruits and Vegetables

Mashed, juiced, grated or sliced, fresh fruits and vegetables are incredibly beneficial to the skin. They are complex blends of natural chemical substances which make available to you such things as carbohydrates, proteins, fats, vitamins, minerals, fruit acids, enzymes and water all of which are beneficial for treating your skin.

Fresh fruits and vegetables are best used in treatment masks or cold poultices. They can be mashed, juiced, grated, or sliced depending on the fruit or vegetable and the type of preparation being made. Fruits and vegetables may also be incorporated into your skin-exfoliating preparations.

Remember to wash your fruits and vegetables before use to remove any soil, microbes and spray residues. Using organically grown produce ensures there will be no concern of pesticide or herbicide residues.

Apple   *(Prunus malus)*

Grated apple is very soothing and smoothing to a dry skin. It contains malic and tartaric acids which gently exfoliate your skin.

Avocado   *(Persea americana)*

Mashed avocado flesh is very soothing, softening and emollient to dry skins. It is rich in natural oils.

Banana   *(Musa sapientum)*

Mashed banana is used in skin care preparations for its soothing and skin softening properties. It contains mucopolysaccharides which improve skin hydration.

Cucumber   *(Cucumis sativus)*

Cucumber slices and juice are very soothing and anti-inflammatory, hydrating and mildly astringent to the skin.

Grapes   *(Vitus species)*

Crushed grapes are very soothing, cooling and toning to the skin.

Lemon   *(Citrus limon)*

Lemon juice is acidic and is used in hair and skin preparations to counteract the alkalinity of soaps and shampoos thus reducing any product build up and irritation which may result from their use. It is also anti-bacterial, astringent, and contains citric acid, making it useful for treating oily and blemished skin. Do not use undiluted.

Lettuce   *(Latuca sativa)*

Lettuce juice is soothing to the skin and promotes the healing of blemishes.

Oats   *(Avena sativa)*

Oat preparations are very soothing to the skin, relieving irritation, inflammation and itching. They are used in bath preparations, cleansing preparations, face masks, face and body scrubs, and soaps. Oatmeal, oat bran, and oat flour can be used in these skin care preparations.

Passionfruit *(Passiflora incarnata)*

Passionfruit pulp is hydrating, softening and refreshing to the skin.

Paw paw or Papaya *(Caria papaya)*

Paw paw flesh is used in face and body masks as a very gentle exfoliant. It contains the enzyme papain which has the ability to dissolve keratin and hence our dead surface skin cells. Green paw paw contains more of this enzyme.

Peach *(Prunus persica)*

Peach slices, juice or pulp can be used to soothe, soften and hydrate dry skin.

Pear *(Prunus communis)*

Pear slices, juice or pulp can be used to soothe, soften and hydrate dry skin.

Pineapple *(Ananas comosus)*

Pineapple flesh or juice is used in face and body masks as an exfoliant. It contains the enzyme bromelain which has the ability to dissolve keratin and hence dead surface skin cells.

Potato *(Solanum tuberosum)*

Potato juice or grated potato is soothing and anti-inflammatory. It reduces bruising and calms puffy eyes.

Rockmelon or cantaloupe *(Cucumis melo cantalupensis)*

Rockmelon slices, pulp or juice are used to hydrate and soothe dry and inflamed skins.

Seaweed *(Fucus vesiculosis)*

There are many varieties of seaweed which are used in thalassotherapy. Thalassotherapy is a term applied to treatments using ingredients from the sea. It is derived from the Greek word, *thalassa* meaning ocean.

Seaweed is used in skin care for its ability to attract and retain moisture and for its cell regenerative properties. It is soothing, hydrating and healing to the skin. The Chinese have used it for healing burns and rashes, the Polynesians for wounds, bruises and swelling, and mariners have used it for its healing properties.

Strawberry *(Fragaria vesca)*

Strawberries can be mashed and juiced to make skin care preparations which are soothing, toning and mildly bleaching.

Strawberry leaves can be made into an infusion and used on an oily skin to balance overactive sebaceous glands

Tomato *(Lycopersicum esculentum)*

Tomato slices or pulp are used in skin care preparations. It has astringent properties which make it useful for the treatment of oily skin.

Watermelon *(Citrullus vulgaris)*

Watermelon slices are very soothing, hydrating and toning to the skin. It is generally recommended for use on normal to oily skins.

Nuts, Seeds, Grains and Pulses

Ground and polished nuts, seeds, grains and pulses make superb granules for your skin-exfoliating preparations. Almond meal, oatmeal, oat flakes, ground lentils, adzuki beans, and rice, semolina, bran and lecithin make suitable granules for this purpose. The finer and softer granules are more suitable for facial preparations and the harder granules are more suitable for places where the skin is hardest and toughest, such as on the feet.

Corn starch, potato starch, rice starch and chick pea flour make soothing, absorbent ingredients for body and foot deodorising powders. They can be combined with pure talc, orris root powder, essential oils and herbs to make luxurious fragrant body powders as well as soothing powders for baby's bottom. They can also be combined to make absorbent dry hair cleansers too.

Vegetable Oils, Fats and Waxes

Skin softening and smoothing describe the emollient properties of pure vegetable oils, fats and waxes. Vegetable oils are used as 'base' or 'carrier' oils in face, body and massage oils. They are used in moisturising preparations to protect the skin and to prevent moisture evaporating from the skin. They supply the skin with essential fatty acids, vitamins and minerals and also make effective hair conditioning treatment oils.

Vegetable oils may be combined for different purposes, depending on their healing properties, consistency and odour.

It is important to use cold-pressed vegetable oils unless otherwise specified as they have been exposed to the least heat and processing and hence contain many unaffected and useful nutrients.

Almond oil, sweet *(Prunis communis dulcis)*

Sweet almond oil is an excellent, all-purpose emollient suitable for most skin types. It can be used in body, face and massage oils and in cleansers, creams and lotions.

Apricot kernel oil *(Prunus armeniaca)*

Apricot kernel oil has very similar constituents to sweet almond oil and is used for similar purposes.

Avocado oil *(Persea americana)*

Avocado oil consists mostly of oleic, linloleic, and linolenic acids. Other constituents include palmitic and palmitoleic acids, lecithin, phytosterol, carotenoids, and a high concentration of vitamins A, D, and E. This oil is obtained from the ripe avocado flesh. It has a rich consistency and has a beautiful deep green colour. Dry skins benefit most from this oil. It also acts as a sun filter.

Cocoa butter *(Theobroma cacao)*

Cocoa butter smells like chocolate and is actually used to make chocolate. It is pressed from roasted cocoa beans. It makes a wonderful emollient and lubricant, softening and protecting dry skins. Use cocoa butter in creams, lotions and ointments.

Coconut oil *(Cocos nucifera)*

It is soft white or slightly yellow in colour and semisolid in consistency. Coconut oil remains relatively stable when exposed to the air as it is highly saturated. It is extracted from copra, the white flesh of the coconut.

Coconut oil is used as a hair and body oil, in creams and ointments. It is often chemically treated to make foaming agents for such things as shampoos and bubble baths. It is, along with palm oil, often used as a major component in vegetable soaps making them hard and giving them very good lathering properties.

Copha

Copha (also known as vegetable shortening) is hydrogenated coconut oil and may be used in making ointments and soaps.

Evening primrose oil *(Oenothera biennis)*

Evening primrose oil contains a high amount of gamma linoleic acid, which is one of the essential fatty acids vital for the maintenance of healthy epidermal cells. It improves the skin's ability to develop normal barrier functions. It is used in the treatment of dry, flaky, sensitive skin conditions such as eczema and psoriasis. As evening primrose oil is rich in essential fatty acids it is important not to expose it to high temperatures.

Jojoba oil *(Simmondsis chinensis)*

Jojoba oil is made up primarily of unsaturated wax esters and is quite resistant to rancidity. It has a very fine consistency and is absorbed readily by the skin. It makes an excellent facial oil and can be used in light, non-greasy moisturising preparations. It is also used as a hair conditioning oil. It was traditionally held in high regard by Native Americans of the Sonora Desert for its cosmetic properties.

Olive oil *(Olea europaea)*

Olive oil is a mono-unsaturated oil, rich in oleic acid. It is expressed from the olive flesh. The best grade comes from the first pressing and is known as extra virgin olive oil. It has a deep green colour, a distinctive odour and is rich in consistency. It is most suitable for dry skins and is used in massage oils, creams, lotions, soaps and hair conditioning preparations. Olive oil is traditionally used in Mediterranean countries.

Rosehip oil *(Rosa rubignosa or Rosa mosqueta)*

Rosehip oil is high in both linoleic and linolenic fatty acids which are believed to be responsible for its ability to encourage regeneration and repair of skin tissue. It is used in the treatment of damaged skin tissue including scars and burns. It improves the texture of dry and wrinkled skins. It has a very fine consistency and makes a wonderful facial oil and can be incorporated into creams. Rosehip oil is produced in Chile and is obtained by solvent extraction. It is extracted from the seeds of a rose bush which grows wild in the southern Andes. As rosehip oil is high in essential fatty acids it is important not to expose it to high temperatures.

Shea butter *(Butyrospermum parkii)*

Karite nut butter, better known as shea butter, is a vegetable fat extracted from the fruit of a tree which grows in Africa. It protects the skin, improves its suppleness and elasticity and promotes skin healing. It makes an excellent ingredient in skin creams and balms, especially for dry, damaged and irritated skins.

Soyabean oil *(Glycine max)*

Soyabean oil is rich in vitamin E and contains more lecithin than any other vegetable oil. It is also high in unsaturated fatty acids. It makes a superb body and massage oil.

Wheatgerm oil *(Triticum durum)*

Wheatgerm oil has a very high vitamin E content. This makes it useful in healing preparations for damaged or scarred skin. It has a distinctive, nutty odour and is rich in consistency. It can be used as a body oil or incorporated into creams.

Choosing a vegetable oil

The pure vegetable oils below have been listed in order of lightest and finest through to heaviest and thickest. This is useful to consider when wanting to choose an oil which is light and easily absorbed or, on the other hand, an oil which is not as readily absorbed and remains on the surface of the skin longer and is more protective. The cold-pressed vegetable oils may be blended if you would like to utilise the properties of several oils or to vary a preparation's consistency and feel on the skin.

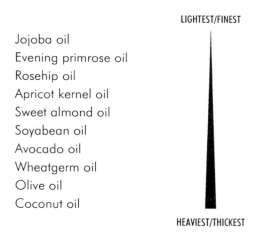

LIGHTEST/FINEST

Jojoba oil
Evening primrose oil
Rosehip oil
Apricot kernel oil
Sweet almond oil
Soyabean oil
Avocado oil
Wheatgerm oil
Olive oil
Coconut oil

HEAVIEST/THICKEST

Herbs

Herbal preparations for your skin and hair can be made from the herbs in your garden or from herbs purchased from shops specialising in high quality dried herbs.

Herbs make available to you many active constituents which can be utilised in the treatment and care of your skin and hair.

Aloe vera *(Aloe vera barbadensis)*

Aloe vera gel is obtained from the plant's succulent leaves. It is an effective healing agent for burns, injuries and acne. The gel is cooling, soothing, hydrating and stimulates the growth of new cells and tissues. It can be incorporated into moisturising preparations or applied directly to the skin.

Calendula *(Calendula officinalis)*

Infusions or tinctures made using the petals of the calendula flower are antiseptic, healing, soothing, and anti-inflammatory. Calendula may be used to treat wounds and burns and sensitive, inflamed skin conditions. It is also used in hair rinses to impart golden highlights to fair hair. Calendula flowers can be used in many preparations including oils, ointments, creams, infusions, poultices and compresses.

Chamomile *(Matricaria chamomilla)*

Chamomile flowers can be made into an infusion and used as a compress to soothe the skin and eyes, reducing inflammation and irritation. An infused oil can also be made from the flowers and is particularly soothing to the skin. Chamomile preparations also improve wound healing. The flowers are also used in hair preparations for fair hair as they contain a substance called apigenin which brightens and adds golden highlights to the hair.

Comfrey *(Symphytum officinale)*

Comfrey leaves and roots contain allantoin and mucilage, among other ingredients, which give them their excellent skin healing and soothing properties. Comfrey can be used in infusions, poultices, ointments and creams.

Elder flowers *(Sambucus nigra)*

Elder flowers are used for their mildly astringent and soothing properties. Elder flower infusions can be used as a skin toner and eye compress. In the nineteenth century, it was commonly recommended to clear the complexion of freckles.

Fennel *(Foeniculum vulgare)*

Fennel seeds can be made into an infusion which can then be used as a compress for inflamed eyes and eyelids.

Ginseng *(Panax ginseng)*

Ginseng is said to aid in increasing skin elasticity and in revitalising and reactivating epidermal cell production. The infusion, or tincture of the root, can be incorporated into moisturisers.

Gotu kola *(Centella asiatica)*

Gotu kola has traditionally been used to improve couperose (fine surface capillaries) conditions. It is healing, soothing and used to relieve irritation. The leaves are used to make an infusion which can be applied directly to the skin, used in a compress or added to a moisturiser. A cool poultice can also be made and applied to the skin. An infused oil made from gotu kola can be applied directly to the skin or incorporated into moisturisers.

Lemon balm *(Melissa officinalis)*

Lemon balm is antiseptic, astringent, soothing and healing. It is used to treat sensitive blemished skins. The infusion or diluted tincture can be used for this purpose. It can be used as a skin toner and wiped over the skin after cleansing.

Lemongrass *(Cymbopogon citratus)*

Lemongrass is used on oily skins to help normalise excessive sebaceous secretions. The infusion or diluted tincture can be used for this purpose. It can be used as a skin toner and wiped over the skin after cleansing.

Liquorice *(Glycyrrhiza glabra)*

Liquorice root preparations are very soothing to the skin and can be used in the treatment of skin inflammations such as eczema.

Marshmallow *(Althaea officinalis)*

Marshmallow root is prepared as a cold infusion. The chopped root is left to steep in water overnight in order to allow for the extraction of mucilage. Heat causes the mucilage to solidify. Mucilage gives marshmallow root its anti-inflammatory, soothing properties. The infusion may be applied to the skin directly or incorporated into moisturisers.

Nettle *(Urtica dioica)*

Stinging nettles sting when they are fresh. However, the dried herb is safe to touch. It encourages circulation and is particularly useful in hair preparations to improve the condition of the hair and scalp.

Orris *(Iris florentina)*

Powdered orris root which comes from the Florentine iris has a delicate fragrance reminiscent of violets. Its absorbent properties make it useful in powders for the body and feet. It also acts as a fixative in perfumes; it contributes a delicate fragrance of its own as well as ensuring a perfume lasts longer on the skin.

Peppermint *(Mentha piperita)*

An infusion made from peppermint leaves relieves skin irritation, inflammation and itching. It has a refreshing and cooling effect which is due to the constriction of capillaries. It is also used in hair care preparations to relieve dandruff.

Rosemary *(Rosmarinus officinalis)*

Rosemary has antiseptic, astringent, deodorant, healing, and stimulating properties. It improves blood circulation and is helpful for devitalised skins. As rosemary stimulates hair follicles and improves scalp conditions, it is used in hair preparations to relieve dandruff and encourage hair growth.

Sage *(Salvia officinalis)*

Sage leaves are used for their astringent, antibacterial, antiseptic, and healing properties. Used over a period of time, sage will begin to darken the hair. It also helps improve dandruff conditions and oily skin with pimples. Sage can be used in baths, in compresses, as a healing skin toner, in hair rinses and in deodorant preparations.

Slippery elm *(Ulmus fulva)*

Powdered slippery elm bark is very soothing, healing and hydrating to the skin. When mixed with water it swells and forms a thick gel-like substance due to its high content of mucilage. It can be used as a poultice or in face masks.

Soapwort *(Saponaria officinalis)*

Soapwort root is used as a mild cleansing agent for the skin and hair. It soothes the skin and relieves itching. It can be used as a cleanser for sensitive and inflamed skins and as a mild cleanser for sensitive and inflamed scalps and fragile hair. Soapwort root produces a mild lather due to its saponin content.

Tea, green *(Camellia sinensis)*

Green tea has been noted to be rich in potent antioxidants called catechins and may provide anti-aging benefits if used with regularity. It also calms sensitive skin and has mild astringent properties.

Thyme *(Thymus vulgaris)*

Thyme leaves are used for their antiseptic, astringent and healing properties. It can be made into an infusion, tincture, herbal vinegar or herbal oil and used in deodorants, shampoos and hair rinses for dandruff and oily hair, aftershaves, skin toners for oily and blemished skin, and in bath preparations.

Yarrow *(Achillea millefolium)*

Yarrow flowers and leaves are used for their anti-inflammatory, antiseptic, astringent and healing properties. They are used to heal wounds, stop bleeding, treat oily and blemished skin and greasy hair. They are used in poultices, compresses and infusions applied directly to the skin and in hair rinses.

Other Ingredients

Alcohol

Alcohol, also known as ethanol, or ethyl alcohol, is manufactured from natural sources via the fermentation of starch, grains, sugar and other carbohydrates. Alcohol may also be derived from petrochemical sources.

Alcohol has antiseptic and preservative properties and is a good solvent. Its solvent properties make it useful in making concentrated herbal extracts. It is also used to help solubilise essential oils into water which is useful when making perfumes and sprays. It is astringent and has a cooling effect on the skin. It has also been used in skin toners, aftershaves, perfumes and toilet waters. It can be drying and irritating to the skin in high concentrations. This can be counteracted in skin care preparations by the incorporation of humectants such as glycerin and emollient oils and fats if, for example, alcoholic herbal extracts are used in creams and lotions.

Vodka is suitable for making home made skin and fragrance preparations. A natural perfume base is available from some aromatherapy suppliers and is made from high grade perfume ethanol which has had orris root or benzoin gum infused into it. This base is ideal for making perfumes, deodorants and body sprays. The orris root or benzoin acts as a 'base' or a 'fixative' in a perfume.

Fatty alcohols, such as cetyl alcohol and cetearyl alcohol, are actually wax-like substances and have a completely different function on the skin and in cosmetic preparations to ethanol. They act as emulsifiers and emollients in creams and lotions. If they are of plant origin, they are usually obtained from coconut or palm oil. Otherwise, they are petrochemically derived.

Constituents in essential oils, such as linalool which is a monoterpene alcohol, contribute to their antiseptic properties.

As you can see, the term alcohol applies to a range of substances. These substances each have a hydroxyl -OH group in their chemical structure. They each have a different function and are very useful when used in appropriate formulations.

Argiletz clays

Argiletz clays are clays with a high mineral content which gives them active properties on the skin such as cleansing, detoxifying, drawing, exfoliating, healing, soothing, and toning. They come from Argiletz in France, are mined at specific depths in areas free from contamination and are sun-dried in order to retain and enhance their healing properties.

The use of clay in preparations to heal the skin is known as pelotherapy. Argiletz clays can be used in masks, poultices, absorbent powders, scalp treatments, and to colour soaps, bath salts and other skin care preparations.

The Argiletz clays are generally available in the following colours which are due to their various mineral contents. This gives each clay its unique healing properties.

Clay	Uses
Green	Is used in preparations such as face masks to help with tissue repair, to draw out toxins and calm inflammation. It is very useful in the treatment of acne.
Yellow	Improves the condition of devitalised and tired looking skin.
Red	Improves the condition of dry, sensitive and capillaried skin.
Pink	Is cleansing and toning to the skin and is suitable for use on all skin types, especially skin losing its tone.
White	Soothes and softens the skin and is suitable for all skin types. It has the gentlest drawing action of all the clays.

Green clay is the most absorbent of the clays, with the clays becoming less absorbent as you move down the list, white clay is the least absorbent and gentlest of the clays.

Apple cider vinegar

Apple cider vinegar helps restore the skin's pH level. It balances oily skin and softens and reduces flakiness in dry skin. It must be diluted before being applied to the skin, 5ml of apple cider vinegar to 40ml of water or one teaspoon of apple cider vinegar to two tablespoons of water. It can be used to make herbal extracts which are then used to make fragrant and healing baths, hair rinses, deodorants and body splashes.

Arrowroot

Arrowroot powder or starch is made from the dried rhizome of the plant. It makes an excellent absorbent body powder and can be used as a thickener in face masks.

Beeswax

Beeswax is one of the oldest raw ingredients used in cosmetic preparations. It serves as an emulsifier in water-in-oil emulsions, regulates a formulation's consistency, acts as a base and stiffener in creams, balms, ointments, lipsticks and pomades. When applied to the skin's surface, it forms a network rather than a totally occlusive film. White beeswax has been bleached while unbleached beeswax can be various shades of brown and yellow.

Bentonite

Bentonite is a naturally occurring mineral, a colloidal aluminium silicate clay. It differs from other clays in that when it is mixed with water it forms a gel. It is used in face masks to combine and suspend active ingredients.

Benzoin tincture

Tincture of benzoin is an alcoholic extract of benzoin gum which comes from the tree Styrax benzoin which grows mainly in Indonesia and Thailand. It has antibacterial properties and anti-oxidant properties. This makes it very useful in helping to preserve creams, lotions and other herbal preparations. It also helps heal broken or cracked skin.

Bicarbonate of soda

Bicarbonate of soda is also known as baking soda and sodium bicarbonate. It is used in baths to soothe itchy skins and can be combined with citric acid to create fun fizzy baths. It is used in hair rinses to remove residue build-up.

Borax

Borax is an alkaline salt which was originally collected from the sea or lake bed after the evaporation of water but it is now mined. It is used with beeswax to form an emulsifier in water-in-oil emulsions. The more borax used, the stiffer an emulsion will become.

Castile soap

Castile soap is available as a hard bar of soap or as a liquid soap. It is named after a place called Castile in Spain where olive oil is produced. Originally Castile soap contained 40-50 per cent olive oil. Now, unfortunately, Castile soap is being sold with concentrations of 20 per cent olive oil. It is made by saponifying olive oil and potassium hydroxide. It is a very mild soap which can be used to wash the body and hair. Especially suitable for sensitive skins.

Caustic soda/caustic potash

Sodium hydroxide/potassium hydroxide. See Lye on page 14.

Champagne/beer

Leftover flat champagne or beer can be used as a hair rinse. After shampooing pour the beer or champagne through your hair, leave on for a few minutes then rinse out. It leaves your hair feeling soft and shiny and gives it body.

Cream

Cream can be used in face masks to soften and soothe dry skins. It is rich in butterfat and contains lecithin. It can also be used as a simple facial massage medium.

Citric acid

Derived by fermentation of sugars from citrus fruits. It is used for its anti-oxidant and preservative properties and to balance the pH of a product.

Essential oil solubiliser

This product is sold by suppliers of aromatherapy products. It is used to disperse essential oils throughout water, including the bath water and aromatic face and body sprays. It will possibly be made from treated vegetable oil or contain alcohol.

Emulsifying wax

Emulsifying wax is an emulsifying agent used in creams and lotions to prevent the water and oil ingredients from separating. There are various types available, including ones derived from treated coconut and palm oils, animal fats or petroleum by-products. They are usually very efficient ensuring emulsions remain stable.

Epsom salts

Epsom salts are mineral salts of magnesium sulphate. They are used for making bath salts to relieve sore and aching muscles as they are detoxifying and relaxing. Epsom salts can also be used in drawing poultices.

Glycerin

Glycerin, also known as glycerine or glycerol, is a clear syrupy liquid. It is obtained from vegetable oils, which is generally more expensive, or animal fats via the process of soap making. It may be produced synthetically from propylene alcohol.

It is a humectant used in moisturisers due to its water-binding capabilities that allow it to draw and absorb water from the air. However, its use has been cautioned in aggressive climatic conditions such as excessive wind, sun and low humidity as it has been found to absorb moisture from the skin. Your preparation should contain no more than 20 per cent glycerin.

Fuller's earth

A clay which is used for its drawing and absorptive properties. Generally used in face masks for oily skin or as a substitute for talc.

Guar gum

Guar gum is a complex carbohydrate, soluble fibre extracted from the guar plant grown in the Middle East. It acts as a thickener, stabiliser and gelling agent.

Honey

Honey has antiseptic, hygroscopic and healing properties. It can be incorporated into face masks and healing ointments and balms and can be applied directly to help heal sores. Ensure that you use unprocessed honey.

Kaolin

Kaolin is also known as China clay and white clay. It was originally only obtained from Mount Kaolin in China. It is available as a white powder and is used in cleansing, drawing masks. It is especially useful for oily skins. It may be used to make body deodorant and foot powders.

Lanolin

Lanolin is the fat removed from sheep's wool. It is secreted by the sheep's sebaceous (oil) glands. It is used in creams for its rich, emollient properties. It is mainly used in preparations for dry skin. Anhydrous (water-free) lanolin is commonly available. It is possible that it may sensitise irritated or sensitive skins, however, it seems to have no negative effect on normal skin.

Lecithin

Lecithin is generally obtained from eggs or soya beans and is available as a thick syrupy substance or in granule form. It is a mixture of stearic, palmitic, and oleic acid compounds and is high in the B vitamins choline and inositol. Lecithin is used as an emollient, emulsifier and anti-oxidant. It attracts water and acts as a moisturiser. Lecithin is used in moisturisers, creams, ointments, face masks and hair conditioners.

Linseeds

Also known as flax seeds, linseeds contain an oil high in essential fatty acids which makes them highly nutritive. Linseeds are also high in mucilage and, when they are soaked in water, they form a soothing gel. Wonderful for soothing and moisturising inflamed, irritated skin.

Loofah

A loofah is the fibrous skeleton of a gourd. It looks like a giant cucumber or zucchini and grows on a vine. Use a loofah in a shower as a body sponge. It is used to exfoliate the skin and to stimulate the circulation in the skin.

Lye

Sodium hydroxide and potassium hydroxide are commonly called caustic soda and potash respectively. Lye is made by mixing either of these two ingredients with water to create a strong alkaline base which reacts with oils and fats to form soap.

Milk

Full cream milk or powdered milk may be used when bathing to soften and soothe the skin. After bathing with milk ensure that you rinse your skin well.

Paraffin

Paraffin wax is used as a beeswax substitute. It is a solid mixture of hydrocarbons obtained from petroleum, wood or coal. Paraffin oil, also known as mineral oil, is used as a substitute for pure vegetable oils. It tends to remain on the surface of the skin and is not recommended for use in aromatherapy preparations as it does not allow for the penetration of pure essential oils in the same way that pure vegetable oils do. Paraffin is a very inexpensive and stable ingredient. It has not been included in any recipes in this book, however, because it is a petrochemically derived ingredient.

Pectin

Pectin is extracted from apples or the inner portion of citrus fruit rind. It is used as a thickening and gelling agent. It is soothing, hydrating and mildly acidic. Pectin is used to make gel face masks.

Petrolatum

Petrolatum is also known as petroleum jelly. It is a purified mixture of semisolid hydrocarbons obtained from petroleum. It is used to soften the skin and prevent moisture loss from the skin. Petrolatum is often recommended for use in moisturisers and as a base for ointments. It has not been included in any of the recipes in this book as it is a petrochemically derived ingredient.

Pumice

Pumice stones are volcanic in origin and they are often seen washed up on beaches. They actually float on water. Pumice can be ground and used in exfoliating preparations or the stones can be used as they are and massaged over your feet to remove dry rough skin. Your feet should be soaked in water to soften the skin first.

Red wine

Red wine contains tartaric acid and can be used on rough skins to smooth and soften the skin. It can be incorporated into face masks.

Sea salt

Sea salt is used as an exfoliant in body scrubs. It is also included in bath salt mixtures. However, it may be drying to the skin if used in bath salts.

Sugar

Granulated sugar is used as an exfoliant in body scrubs. It is also the main ingredient in 'sugaring', an excellent alternative to wax for hair removal.

Talc

Talc is generally made from finely ground magnesium silicate, a mineral. It is also known as French chalk. It is used for its absorbent properties, to provide lubrication, as a bulking agent, and as an opacifying agent. As the particles are very fine, it is best not used long term around the genital area or where it can be inhaled by babies.

Tallow

Tallow is the fat which remains after beef fat has been purified to remove any meat or sinew. It is commonly used in commercial soap making.

Xanthan gum

Xanthan gum is also known as corn sugar gum. This polysaccharide is produced from the bacteria (*Xathomonas campestris*) being fermented with corn sugar. It is used as a thickener, emulsifier and gelling agent.

Yeast

Yeast is a type of fungus, and brewer's yeast is the yeast most often used in skin care. It is very stimulating and can be incorporated into face masks for devitalised skins. It is not recommended for use on sensitive skins.

Yoghurt

Yoghurt is made by the action of certain types of beneficial bacteria on milk. It is very soothing, cooling and hydrating to the skin. Yoghurt makes an excellent base for face and body masks especially for inflamed, irritated skin and can be used on all skin types.

Zinc

Zinc oxide is a white powder which is added to ointments and balms for its soothing, astringent and protective properties. It is often used in nappy rash preparations and in sunscreens as it offers protection from ultraviolet (UV) rays.

Infused Oils

Infused oils are generally made by macerating plant material in a fixed oil, usually a vegetable oil, over some time to allow the active constituents of the plant to pass into the fixed oil. In some cases the fixed oil and plant matter are heated to speed up the process. The plant material is then strained and filtered out of the preparation. The resulting oil can then be used directly on the skin or incorporated into creams, ointments or treatment oil blends.

Arnica oil *(Arnica montana)*

Arnica flowers are used to make arnica infused oil. It is dark green in colour and is used in the treatment of bruises, swelling and sprains.

Calendula oil *(Calendula officinalis)*

Calendula flowers are used to make calendula infused oil. It is a beautiful orange colour and is healing and soothing to the skin. Calendula oil can be used in preparations for rashes and inflamed skin conditions such as eczema and dermatitis, for wound healing and to reduce scarring.

Carrot oil *(Daucus carota)*

Carrot roots are used in the making of carrot infused oil. Carrot oil is a beautiful deep orange colour, is rich in beta-carotene (vitamin A) and is used to rejuvenate dry and mature skin conditions.

Hypericum oil *(Hypericum perforatum)*

Hypericum is also commonly known as St John's wort. The aerial parts of the herb are used to make this oil. It is deep red in colour due to its hypericin content. Hypericum oil is used in the treatment of inflamed, irritated skin conditions, for burns and bruises, and for wound healing.

Do not apply this oil to areas of the skin which will be exposed to the sun as it may photosensitise the skin and cause the skin to burn more quickly.

Floral Waters

Authentic floral waters are also known as waters of distillation or aromatic hydrosols. They are the by-product of essential oil distillation.

Once the distilled essential oil has been removed from the water, we are left with traces of water soluble essential oil constituents in the remaining water. These constituents generally have anti-inflammatory and antiseptic properties. This makes floral waters suitable for use in soothing, healing compresses for inflamed eyes and skin.

They also make excellent skin toners and fresheners and can be incorporated into moisturising preparations. They have a very subtle fragrance reminiscent of the essential oil.

It is important to be aware that there are floral waters, such as rosewater or orange flower water, which have been made by blending food or fragrance essences into water. They do not contain the water soluble components of the pure essential oil and yet are still called pure floral waters. They are usually sold for flavouring food and are generally inexpensive. These floral waters are not suitable for making good quality skin care preparations.

Chamomile water *(Matricaria chamomilla)*

Chamomile water is very soothing. It is suitable for use on sensitive and inflamed eyes and skin.

Lavender water *(Lavendula angustifolia)*

Lavender water is soothing and antiseptic. It helps soothe and heal blemished skin.

Orange flower water *(Citrus aurantium var. amara)*

Orange flower water is also known as neroli water. It has soothing and slightly astringent properties and is suitable for combination and sensitive skin.

Rosewater *(Rosa damascena)*

Rosewater is soothing and cooling to the skin. It can be used on all skin types, especially dry and sensitive skin.

Witch-hazel water *(Hamamelis virginiana)*

Witch-hazel water is soothing and antiseptic. It is especially useful on oily, blemished skin.

Base Products

Base products are pre-made preparations into which herbal extracts and/or essential oils may be added. They are simple preparations and do not contain fragrances, colouring agents, essential oils or herbal extracts. This allows you to customise a preparation for a particular purpose very easily and quickly. The following suggested quantities of ingredients to be added to the base products are given as a guideline. You may want to check with your supplier for any variations.

Base Product	Quantity of Active Ingredients
Shampoo	Herbal decoctions and infusions, essential oils, and vegetable oils can all be added to a shampoo base. To make a shampoo for your hair, see the section on Hair Shampoos (page 122) for recipes.
Body wash and liquid Castile soap	To make an aromatherapy body wash, add 20 drops of essential oil to each 100ml of body wash base or liquid Castile soap.
Moisture cream	Essential oils, infused oils, vegetable oils, herbal extracts (fluid extracts, tinctures) and floral waters may be added to a cream base. To each 100ml of cream base, the following quantities of ingredients may be added. • Essential oils — up to 1ml (20 drops) for a face cream or cream for a baby, up to 2.5ml (50 drops) for a body cream • Infused oils and vegetable oils — up to 5ml • Herbal extracts (fluid extracts, tinctures) — up to 5ml • Floral waters — up to 20ml A combination of these ingredients may be added to your base cream. If doing so, it is important to reduce the quantity of each one as the final preparation may separate.
Dispersing bath oil	Pure essential oils can be added to a dispersing bath oil base to create an aromatherapy bath oil. Add up to 3ml (60 drops) of pure essential oil to each 100ml of dispersing bath oil base. For aromatherapy bath oil recipes, see the section on Bath Oils (page 104).
Bubble bath	Pure essential oils can be added to a bubble bath base to create an aromatherapy bubble bath. Add up to 1ml (20 drops) of pure essential oil to each 100ml of bubble bath base. For aromatherapy bubble bath recipes, see the section on Bubble Baths (page 103).

Aromatherapy

Your skin and hair will benefit from the pure essential oils used in your preparations. Applied topically, not only do the essential oils benefit the skin, but they may also penetrate the skin and be absorbed into the bloodstream where they have further therapeutic benefits. Their odoriferous molecules are inhaled which means the essential oils can affect us on an emotional and mental level. How wonderful.

Aromatherapy Skin Benefits

Essential oils specifically benefit your skin and hair in the following ways. They:

- support and balance skin functions;

- stimulate healthy skin cell production and regeneration. They can be used to aid skin healing when it has been damaged through wounding or through long-term damage, such as from sun exposure which is evidenced in aging skin;

- improve skin hydration;

- balance sebum production;

- improve circulation in the skin thereby improving the flow of nutrients and oxygen to the skin as well as the elimination of waste (this property also aids in the dispersion of bruises);

- calm and soothe redness, irritation, itchiness and inflammation;

- act as antiseptics, are fungicidal and can be used to treat skin infections;

- have astringent properties;

- relax and relieve tension;

- smell divine.

Essential Oil Dilution

In order to use your essential oils safely and effectively, it is important to use the correct quantity of essential oil in each type of preparation.

Product	Essential Oil Dilution
Facial oils, face creams	1 per cent dilution when using essential oils therapeutically to treat skin conditions. 0.25-0.5 per cent dilution for long-term use. This low dilution is recommended to prevent the skin from becoming sensitised to a particular essential oil.
Facial gels	0.25 per cent dilution or less is recommended when making a gel.
Direct or neat application	Lavender or tea-tree oil may be applied directly to a pimple, mosquito bite, wart or cold sore. Do not wipe over the face or over large areas of skin.
Masks	0.5 per cent dilution especially if the mask contains no vegetable oil.
Eye oils and eye creams	Avoid using essential oils or use a 0.25 per cent dilution or less. Ensure the oils you have chosen are non-sensitising or non-stimulating essential oils. The skin around the eyes is particularly thin and sensitive and there is the possibility of essential oils being rubbed into or seeping into the eyes.
Body products	1-3 per cent dilution is generally considered a safe and effective dilution for body oils, creams, lotions, ointments and balms depending on their purpose.
Compresses	Add three to five drops of pure essential oil to 500ml of water. When wanting to calm an inflamed skin condition, use cool water and re-dip the cloth in the cool water whenever the skin feels as though it is heating up. When using a compress on aching muscles use warm/hot water and re-dip the cloth in the warm/hot water when the cloth begins to cool down.
Bath oils and bath salts	1-3 per cent dilution is generally considered to be safe. A lower dilution is recommended when treating inflamed skin conditions and a higher dilution is recommended when making bath preparations for aching muscles.
Foaming products	Foaming products may include unscented bubble baths, shampoos and body washes. A 0.5-1 per cent dilution is recommended. Higher concentrations than this will result in the product's lathering or foaming properties being reduced.
Sensitive skin products	0.5-1 per cent dilution. Essential oil dilution in some particularly sensitive and inflamed conditions may be even less. Your choice of essential oils to be applied to this particular skin type should be made carefully.
Baby products	0.25-1 per cent dilution. It is important to use a very low dilution of essential oils on babies due to their sensitive skins and their body size. Your choice of essential oils for babies is also limited to very safe oils such as blue and Roman chamomile, lavender, mandarin, tangerine and neroli.

Precautions

- Ensure that you are using the finest quality pure essential oils, not perfume, perfume oils, fragrance oils or pure essential oils intended for the fragrance industry, the food industry or household products.
- Do not apply pure essential oils directly onto the skin or take internally unless advised by a qualified practitioner.
- Never exceed the recommended dose or dilutions.
- Do not use the same oil all the time. Use a blend of oils or alternate your essential oils from week to week.

Pregnancy

Many aromatherapists consider it is sensible to avoid the use of the following commonly available essential oils during pregnancy, especially during the first three months.

> Aniseed, basil, clary sage, Virginian and Atlas cedarwood, cypress, sweet and bitter fennel, hyssop, jasmine, juniper, sweet marjoram, myrrh, nutmeg, pennyroyal, peppermint, rose, rosemary, sage and thyme.

High blood pressure

Many aromatherapists consider it is sensible to avoid the use of the following essential oils for anyone with hypertension:

> Hyssop, rosemary, sage and thyme.

Photosensitivity

The following oils may cause the skin to burn if exposed to strong ultra violet light from any source, including the sun:

> Angelica root, bergamot, cold pressed lime, bitter orange and lemon.

Skin irritations

The following oils may cause skin irritations on sensitive skins. Sensitivity varies from person to person and from oil to oil:

> Basil, lemon, cinnamon leaf and bark, clove bud, lemongrass, thyme and tea tree.

Pure Essential Oils

Bergamot (*Citrus aurantium* subsp. *bergamia*)

Bergamot has antiseptic and wound healing properties. It is used to treat seborrhoea of the skin and scalp including acne, oily hair and skin. It is also used in formulae for eczema and psoriasis.

Black pepper (*Piper nigrum*)

Black pepper has rubefacient properties which means it stimulates local circulation. This makes it useful, when used in small quantities, for dispersing bruises.

Carrot seed (*Daucus carota*)

Carrot seed improves the circulation in the skin and has skin healing properties. It is used to improve skin tone in mature skins, couperose (fine surface capillaries), wounds, eczema and psoriasis.

Cedarwood, Atlas (*Cedrus atlantica*)

Atlas cedarwood has antiseptc, astringent and wound healing properties. It is very useful in treating acne and oily skin, dandruff and oily hair. It is also used as an insect repellent.

Chamomile, blue *(Matricaria recutita)*

Blue chamomile, also known as German chamomile, has proven anti-inflammatory properties, is antiseptic and has skin healing properties. It calms red, inflamed, irritated skin conditions including acne, dermatitis, eczema and psoriasis. It is suitable for all skin types including sensitive skin. Chamomile is an excellent choice for use on babies.

Cistus *(Cistus ladaniferus)*

Cistus, also known as rock rose, has antiseptic, astringent and skin healing properties. It is used to heal infected and inflamed skin conditions including acne, eczema, psoriasis, wounds and herpes lesions. It also improves the condition of mature skin.

Citronella *(Cymbopogon nardus)*

Citronella is useful for combatting excessive perspiration and oily skin. It is also an effective insect repellent.

Clary sage *(Salvia sclarea)*

Clary sage has antiseptic, astringent and skin healing properties and regulates excess sebum production. It is used to treat acne, oily hair and skin and dandruff.

Cypress *(Cupressus sempervirens)*

Cypress has antiseptic, astringent, deodorant, and vaso-constrictive properties. It helps improve venous tone and is used in the treatment of varicose veins, spider veins and broken capillaries. Cypress can also be used to reduce excess oiliness and perspiration.

Everlasting *(Helichrysum angustifolium)*

Everlasting, also known as immortelle, has anti-inflammatory, antiseptic, astringent and skin healing properties. It is used to treat sensitive, inflamed skins, eczema and psoriasis. Everlasting is also used to heal wounds as well as reduce old scar tissue and stretch marks.

Frankincense *(Boswellia carteri)*

Frankincense has antiseptic, astringent, regenerative, and skin healing properties. It is used to improve the tone of mature and damaged skin, to heal wounds and reduce scars and excess oiliness.

Geranium *(Pelargonium graveolens)*

Geranium has antiseptic, astringent and skin healing properties. It helps regulate sebum production, making it especially useful for oily and combination skin, although it is beneficial for all skin types. Geranium encourages wound healing and is also used to improve broken capillaries, spider veins and varicose veins.

Jasmine *(Jasminum grandiflorum)*

Jasmine has anti-inflammatory, antiseptic and skin healing properties. It is used to soothe inflamed skin and to improve the condition of mature skin. Jasmine is usually available as an absolute which means it is obtained via solvent extraction.

Lavender *(Lavendula angustifolia)*

Lavender has anti-inflammatory, antiseptic and skin healing properties. It is especially successful in the treatment of burns whether they be from hot objects, liquids or the sun. Lavender is particularly soothing for inflamed skin conditions such as eczema, dermatitis and psoriasis and is used to encourage wound healing. Acne conditions benefit from lavender's anti-inflammatory, antiseptic and skin healing properties. It is also used to relieve itching and can be used as an effective insect repellent.

Lemon *(Citrus limon)*

Lemon has antiseptic, astringent, wound healing and mild circulatory stimulating properties. It also helps to dissolve sebum. Lemon is used to treat oily, congested skin and devitalised skin. Its astringent and mild circulatory stimulating properties improve the condition of varicose veins.

Mandarin/Tangerine (*Citrus reticulata*)

Mandarin or tangerine essential oils are used in blends to help prevent stretch marks.

Myrrh (*Commiphora myrrha*)

Myrrh has anti-inflammatory, antiseptic, astringent, regenerative, skin and wound healing properties. It is used to heal wounds and ulcers, weeping eczema, tinea, and deep cracks on the heels and hands. Myrrh's regenerative properties also make it useful in improving the condition of mature skin.

Neroli (*Citrus aurantium var. amara*)

Neroli is used for its antiseptic and skin healing properties. It is suitable for use on all skin types and assists in treating sensitive, inflamed skin, and broken capillaries.

Palmarosa (*Cymbopogon martinii*)

Palmarosa has antiseptic, skin healing and hydrating properties. It is used to improve the condition of dehydrated skin. Its antiseptic and skin healing properties make it useful in treating acne, eczema, herpes, infected skin conditions and wounds.

Patchouli (*Pogostemon patchouli*)

Patchouli has anti-inflammatory, antiseptic, astringent, regenerative and skin healing properties. It stimulates the growth of skin cells and assists in the formation of scar tissue. It assists in the healing of rough, cracked skin, sores and wounds. It is used in the treatment of acne, eczema, mature skin, fungal infections and scalp disorders. Patchouli also makes a wonderful deodorant.

Peppermint (*Mentha piperita*)

Peppermint has analgesic, antiseptic, astringent and vaso-constrictive properties. It can be used to relieve any kind of skin inflammation, irritation or itching. For this purpose it is used in a 1 per cent dilution or less, otherwise the irritation may be made worse. It may be used to relieve the pain of sunburn and shingles and the itching of dermatitis and eczema. It cools the skin by constricting the capillaries and makes a very refreshing skin tonic.

Petitgrain (*Citrus aurantium var. amara*)

Petitgrain has antiseptic, astringent and deodorant properties. This makes it useful in treating acne, oily skin and hair and excessive perspiration.

Rose (*Rosa damascena and Rosa centifolia*)

Rose has antiseptic, astringent, regenerative and skin healing properties. It may be used on all skin types but especially mature skins. Its astringent properties make it useful for strengthening surface capillaries in conditions such as couperose. Its healing properties encourage wound healing. Rose is commonly available as rose otto, which is obtained via distillation of the rose petals, or rose absolute, which is obtained via solvent extraction.

Rosemary (*Rosmarinus officinalis*)

Rosemary is astringent and stimulates the circulation. It has traditionally been used in the treatment of hair and scalp conditions, such as dandruff and hair loss.

Sandalwood (*Santalum album*)

Sandalwood has antiseptic and hydrating properties. It encourages the retention of moisture within the skin layers and this makes it useful in the treatment of dehydrated skin. Its antiseptic and anti-inflammatory properties also make it useful for the treatment of acne and oily skin, and wounds.

Thyme *(Thymus vulgaris)*

Thyme has antiseptic, astringent and wound healing properties. It is used to treat acne, boils, cuts and wounds, oily skin and skin infections. Sweet thyme (*Thymus vulgaris*, chemotype linalool) is particularly good for healing and treating infections on sensitive and inflamed skin.

Tea tree *(Melaleuca alternifolia)*

Tea tree has anti-fungal, anti-bacterial, antiseptic, and wound healing properties. It is also an effective insect repellent. Tea tree is used in the treatment of acne, cold sores (herpes), dandruff, infected wounds, insect bites, rashes and tinea.

Vetiver *(Vetiveria zizanoides)*

Vetiver has antiseptic properties, stimulates the circulation and encourages wound healing. It is useful in treating acne, oily skin, wounds and devitalised skin.

Yarrow *(Achillea millefolium)*

Yarrow has anti-inflammatory, antiseptic, astringent and wound healing properties. It is used to treat wounds, sores and injuries, acne, eczema, inflamed and irritated skin and sensitive skin.

Ylang ylang *(Cananga odorata)*

Ylang ylang has antiseptic properties and has a balancing effect on sebum production. This makes it suitable for both oily and dry skin. It has been used in hair dressing preparations to help promote healthy hair growth and improve scalp conditions.

From the following pure essential oil compositions, select the most appropriate for your skin type. The quantities specified should be added to 100ml of base preparation. Once you become familiar with the essential oils, you may like to make up your own personalised composition.

Pure Essential Oil Compositions

Normal skin
5 drops ylang ylang
6 drops jasmine absolute
9 drops geranium

Sensitive skin
6 drops blue chamomile
4 drops everlasting

Dry skin
6 drops rose absolute/otto
6 drops palmarosa
8 drops rosewood

Broken capillaries
12 drops cypress
8 drops blue chamomile

Oily skin
12 drops lemon
4 drops geranium
4 drops juniper

Combination skin
6 drops grapefruit
4 drops petitgrain
4 drops geranium
4 drops patchouli

Dehydrated skin
10 drops sandalwood
6 drops lavender
4 drops ylang ylang

Mature skin
6 drops frankincense
12 drops rose absolute/otto
2 drops patchouli

Acne skin
3 drops blue chamomile
8 drops lavender
5 drops palmarosa
4 drops tea tree

Devitalised skin
6 drops rosemary
10 drops lemongrass
4 drops vetiver

Herbal Preparations

When making your herbal preparations, keep in mind that herbs vary in their density. The quantities given in each of these preparations are standard. However, if the herb is particularly lightweight you may find that you will have to reduce the quantity used as the quantity of liquid required will not cover the herb.

Herbal Infusions

Infusions are very simple preparations to make. If you have ever made a cup of tea, you have made an infusion. The softer and more delicate parts of the plant are used to make an infusion. This includes the flowers and leaves. Active constituents are readily extracted from these parts of the plant. Cut or crush the herb into small pieces before making the infusion.

Making an infusion

1. Pour 250ml of boiling water over 15gm of dried herb or 45gm of fresh herb.

2. Place a lid on the teapot or a plate over the cup or jug to ensure minimal loss of volatile substances such as essential oils.

3. Allow the herb to steep for ten to 15 minutes.

4. Strain the herb material out of the infusion and filter if necessary.

The infusion may be used on the skin either warm or cool depending on its purpose.

Herbal Decoctions

The preparation of a decoction is similar to an infusion except that the herb material is boiled. This is necessary when extracting active constituents from the harder parts of the plant such as the roots, wood, bark, seeds and berries. However, an infusion can be made from these parts of the plant if they are finely powdered. When making a decoction, ensure that the roots, wood or bark are chopped up well and that any seeds or berries are crushed.

Making a decoction

1. Put 15gm of dried herb or 45gm of fresh herb and 300ml of water (which reduces down) into a saucepan.

2. Bring to the boil and simmer for 20 minutes. Do this with a lid on the saucepan.

3. Remove from the heat and let the mixture stand for ten minutes.

4. Strain the herb material out of the decoction and filter if necessary.

The herbal decoction may be used on the skin either warm or cool depending on its purpose.

Your infusion or decoction is now ready for immediate use or can be preserved for later use by the addition of 100ml of vodka. If you intend keeping your infusion or decoction for later use, strain the liquid through muslin first, then through coffee filter paper to remove any loose plant material before adding the vodka.

Herbal Syrups

Herbal syrups are made by combining an infusion or decoction with honey or sugar. In skin-care preparations honey is preferable as it is beneficial to the skin. The honey also acts to help preserve the infusion or decoction.

Making a herbal syrup

1. Pour 250ml of the filtered infusion or decoction into a saucepan along with 250gm of honey.
2. Stir the honey into the infusion or decoction until it has dissolved.
3. Gently simmer the mixture until it has a syrupy consistency.
4. Allow the mixture to cool.
5. Once the mixture is cold, store in a dark glass bottle and stopper with a cork in case fermentation occurs and pressure builds up inside the bottle.

Herbal Tinctures

Tinctures are herbal extracts made using alcohol and water. The herbs are steeped in water and alcohol over a period of time in order to extract their active constituents. The mixture of water and alcohol will extract a broader range of active constituents from the herbs than just the water in an infusion or decoction. A tincture is more concentrated than an infusion or decoction. There is no heat involved and tinctures will keep for at least two years.

When making a tincture for use in skin care preparations, vodka is most useful. The minimum concentration of alcohol needed in a herbal tincture to keep it preserved is around 25-30 per cent and vodka is readily available with an alcohol concentration close to this amount. It is also relatively odourless and does not contain unsuitable additives.

Making a tincture

1. Place 250ml of vodka and 50gm of finely cut or ground dried herb or 150gm of chopped fresh herb into a glass container with a lid.
2. Place in a cool place and leave for two weeks shaking it daily.
3. After two weeks strain and filter the tincture firstly through muslin and then through coffee filter paper and store in a dark glass bottle.

Herbal Infused Oils

Infused oils are made by placing herbs into a vegetable carrier oil and allowing the active constituents, such as essential oils and resins, to be extracted by the oil. There are hot and cold methods of making infused oils. The hot method may be used for the leafier parts of the herb and the cold method should be used for delicate flowers.

Making a cold-infused oil

1. Fill a glass jar loosely with fresh chopped herbs and/or whole flowers of your choice or half fill with dried herbs and/or flowers.

2. Cover the herbs with a cold-pressed vegetable oil of your choice, preferably one with as little odour as possible, until the jar is full.
   Jojoba oil is particularly suitable as it does not turn rancid. However, it is often twice the price of other vegetable oils such as sweet almond oil or apricot kernel oil which may also be used.

3. Secure the lid.

4. Leave in a warm place for two weeks. If the jar is placed in direct sunlight, especially in summer, the vegetable oil is likely to turn rancid.

5. Shake twice daily.

6. Strain the mixture through muslin or a double layer of cheesecloth. If you feel the infused oil is not strong enough, repeat the process with a fresh lot of herbs and/or flowers.
   Delicate flowers such as jasmine and honeysuckle should be strained and replaced daily as they decompose quickly.

7. Pour the strained oil into a jar and keep in the fridge. After a few days you will see sediment at the bottom of the jar. Carefully decant the oil into a glass bottle, leaving the small amount of sediment containing oil behind.

8. Refrigerate the infused oil until you are ready to use it.

Making a hot-infused oil

The following method is not suitable for use with delicate flowers such as jasmine or honeysuckle.

1. Place 125gm of dried herbs or 375gm of fresh herbs into a heat-resistant bowl and pour 250ml of cold-pressed vegetable oil over the herbs.

2. Put the bowl into a saucepan of simmering water and gently allow the herbs to infuse for about three hours.

3. Once the oil has cooled, continue as for the cold infused method from step 6.

Herbal Vinegars

Making a herbal vinegar

1. Fill a jar loosely with fresh chopped herbs and/or flowers of your choice or half fill a jar with dried herbs.

2. Pour in enough vinegar to fill the jar. Apple cider vinegar is the best choice of vinegar for skin and hair preparations.

3. Secure the lid.

4. Leave in a warm place for two weeks.

5. Shake twice daily.

6. Strain and filter the vinegar. If you feel the herbal vinegar is not strong enough, repeat the process with a fresh lot of herbs and/or flowers.

7. Pour into a bottle and store in a cool place until ready for use. Store in a refrigerator in hot weather.

Using Herbal Extracts

Many skin care preparations can be made using herbal extracts. Infusions, decoctions, syrups, tinctures, herbal infused oils and vinegars are loaded with active ingredients which can treat and improve the condition of your skin. Please note that the addition of herbal infusions and decoctions will reduce the life of your preparations due to their high water content and plant matter. Preparations made using infusions and decoctions should be used within a couple of days.

Product	Herbal Extract
Skin toners/ fresheners	Infusions and decoctions can be used directly on your skin as skin toners or fresheners. They can be wiped over your face with cotton wool or misted over your face from a spray bottle. Herbal vinegars make excellent skin toners. Add one teaspoon to a glass of water and wipe or spray over your face.
Face masks	Infusions, decoctions and syrups can be mixed with clays, gums, starches and flours to make face masks.
Creams	Infusions, decoctions, syrups, tinctures and infused oils can be incorporated into creams and moisturising preparations.
Deodorants	Infusions and decoctions, herbal vinegars and tinctures, which are made using antiseptic, astringent and fragrant herbs, can be used in deodorant preparations.
Colognes and aftershaves	Fragrant infusions and decoctions, herbal vinegars and tinctures can be used in formulae for colognes and those which are also astringent, healing and soothing can be used in or as aftershave preparations.
Hair rinses	Herbal infusions, decoctions and vinegars can be used as hair rinses to treat scalp problems or to add highlights to and condition the hair.
Bath preparations	Infusions, decoctions, tinctures, herbal vinegars and infused oils can be added to the bath water and foot baths for their therapeutic effects and their fragrance.
Compresses and fomentations	Soothing, healing compresses and fomentations can be made using infusions and decoctions.
Ointments	Tinctures and infused oils can be incorporated into ointments.

Fomentations

Fomentation is the traditional word used for a hot compress. To make a fomentation, soak a cloth or towel in a hot infusion or decoction, wring out the excess liquid and apply while still hot to the affected area of skin. Reapply the fomentation several times as it begins to cool down.

Fomentations which are not excessively hot can be placed over the face to soften the skin, soften sebum build-up and encourage perspiration. This can be performed once or twice a week during a facial and after cleansing.

Ginger is commonly used in fomentations to create warmth and stimulate the circulation especially over sore joints and muscles which benefit from heat.

Compresses

Soak a cloth or towel in an infusion or decoction that has cooled, wring out the excess liquid, and apply to the affected area of skin. Reapply the compress several times as it begins to warm up.

Compresses are used to reduce inflammation and irritation. A soothing cream may be applied afterwards.

The term compress, these days seems to refer to a fomentation as well and is defined as either a hot or cold compress.

Chamomile is commonly used in compresses for inflamed skins.

Poultices

A poultice is a moist, hot herb pack applied to the skin.

If using a fresh herb, crush it into a pulpy mass and warm it up. If using a dried herb, mix it with hot water into a paste. The addition of a small amount of slippery elm powder may be useful to bind the herb material together.

A poultice may be applied directly to the skin or between two pieces of gauze or similar material. This may then be covered with a hot damp cloth or wrapped in cling film.

- **Comfrey** is commonly used in poultices to encourage skin healing and bone healing.
- **Slippery elm** and **linseeds** are often used to draw out boils.
- Bruised **cabbage leaves** are also used in drawing poultices.

Boil treatment poultice

Boils are acute, tender, perifollicular inflammatory nodules resulting from infection by staphylococci. Spreading of infection and reinfection can occur very easily. Boils on the neck and facial area must be treated by a health professional to prevent serious infection complications.

To bring a boil to a head and allow it to drain spontaneously:

1. Mix linseed meal with boiling water to form a thick paste.
2. Allow the mixture to cool slightly so that the heat is bearable to the skin.
3. Apply the mixture to the boil between two pieces of gauze.
4. Wrap with cling film to retain the heat.
5. Remove after ten minutes to allow for expulsion of pus.

Antiseptic lotion for boils

Apply this antiseptic lotion to the boil and skin surrounding it before using the poultice and after the boil has expelled its pus. Apply to the boil regularly at other times.

50ml myrrh tincture
5ml tea tree pure essential oil

Disposal of all materials used in this procedure is important to prevent further infection or reinfection.

Ointments and Balms

Ointments and balms are made from oils, waxes and fats and contain no water. They tend to remain on the surface of the skin longer than a cream and afford some protection to the skin as is the case with lip balms, hand balms and nappy rash balms.

Herbal Ointments and Balms

Herbal ointment and balm base

These ingredients are the basis for making both herbal and aromatherapy ointments and balms.

15-20gm beeswax or cocoa butter
80 to 85ml vegetable oil

Sweet almond oil, apricot kernel oil and jojoba oil are the oils of choice as they remain relatively stable when heated. Olive oil and coconut oil may also be used. However, their consistency is thicker and they are not as easily absorbed by the skin.

Alternatively, simply use 100gm of shea butter in lieu of the above ingredients. Vegetable oil, beeswax and cocoa butter are relatively inexpensive, however, shea butter is very soothing and softening for the skin.

Useful herbs

The following herbs are commonly used to make ointments and balms.

- **Arnica** — bruising and swelling.
- **Calendula** — soothing and healing for eczema, dermatitis, nappy rash and wounds.
- **Chickweed** — soothing and healing for rashes and inflammations including eczema, dermatitis and wounds.
- **Comfrey** — soothing and healing for cuts, wounds, skin damage.
- **Cucumber** — soothing for inflamed skins.
- **Yarrow** — healing for cuts and wounds.

Herbal ointment 1

1. Gently heat the herb with the oil until it loses its normal colour (use just enough herb so that it is well covered by the oil). This indicates that all active constituents have been absorbed by the oil.

2. Strain the herb out of the oil.

3. Melt the beeswax or cocoa butter and add the herbal oil.

4. Stir the ingredients together.

5. Pour into glass jars.

Herbal ointment 2

Trituration is a method of making a herbal ointment by mixing a finely powdered herb into an ointment base. Either melt the base ingredients first and stir in the powder or, if the ointment is soft enough, just stir in the powder.

Herbal ointment 3

1. Melt the vegetable oil and beeswax or cocoa butter together.
2. Add 10ml of herbal tincture, stirring it in thoroughly.
3. Pour into glass jars.

Herbal ointment 4

This is by far the easiest method of making a herbal ointment or balm.

1. Melt the beeswax or cocoa butter and a pre-made herbal infused oil (in place of just vegetable oil) together.
2. Mix thoroughly.
3. Pour into glass jars.

Aromatherapy Ointments and Balms

Aromatherapy ointments and balms can be used as massage balms, healing ointments or perfume balms.

Aromatherapy ointment and balm base

These ingredients are the basis for making both herbal and aromatherapy ointments and balms.

15-20gm beeswax or cocoa butter
20-100 drops (1-5ml) pure essential oil
80-85ml vegetable oil

Sweet almond oil, apricot kernel oil and jojoba oil are the oils of choice as they remain relatively stable when heated. Olive oil and coconut oil may also be used, however their consistency is thicker and they are not as easily absorbed by the skin.

Alternatively, simply use 100gm of shea butter in lieu of the above ingredients. Vegetable oil, beeswax and cocoa butter are relatively inexpensive, however, shea butter is very soothing and softening to the skin.

Aromatherapy ointment or balm

1. Melt the beeswax or cocoa butter with the vegetable oil (or shea butter).
2. Once this mixture starts to cool, add the essential oils and stir in thoroughly.
3. Pour into glass jars, cap and label.

Gels

Gel preparations are used to hydrate, soothe and cool the skin. Hair gels can be made to style your hair. Gels are a great way to introduce essential oils to the skin where a base with oil in it is not desired.

Gels can be made from several plants, most commonly linseeds, pectin (from citrus peel), guar gum, xanthan gum (from corn starch).

Pre-made, commercially available, aloe vera gel can make a suitable gel base as it is or modified for different purposes.

Gel moisturisers

Dilute two per cent (2gm in each 100ml water) pectin or guar or xanthan gum in water following the directions in the 'Plant gels' recipe on this page.

Gels make excellent moisturisers for oily skin as they are oil-free. A small quantity of vegetable oil or infused oil may be blended into the gel if desired. It can also be used under a moisturiser as a skin treatment or it can be used as an aromatherapy pick-me-up for your skin throughout the day.

Eye gels

Dilute two per cent (2gm in each 100ml water) pectin or guar or xanthan gum in water following the directions in the 'Plant gels' recipe on this page.

Eye gels soothe and refresh tired, puffy or irritated eyes. A small quantity of glycerin, or appropriate infused oil or cold pressed vegetable oil may be added for their moisturising and skin softening properties.

Blemish gels

Dilute two per cent (2gm in each 100ml water) pectin or guar or xanthan gum in water following the directions in the 'Plant gels' recipe on this page.

Essential oils which are anti-inflammatory, healing and antiseptic can be added to this gel to help clear the skin of pimples and prevent worsening break-outs.

Gel masks

Dilute three per cent (3gm in each 100ml water) pectin or guar or xanthan gum in water following the directions in the 'Plant gels' recipe on this page.

Gel masks help hydrate the skin as the moisture is held against the skin for some time.

Hair gels

Dilute four to five per cent (4-5gm in each 100ml water) pectin or guar or xanthan gum in water following the directions in the 'Plant gels' recipe on this page.

Plant gels

Plant gels can be made by adding to water one of the following gums: pectin, guar or xanthan.

2-5gm powdered gum
100ml purified water

1. Sprinkle the pectin, guar or xanthan gum slowly into water (floral waters are an excellent choice) which has been heated to 35-40°C.

2. Use a whisk or electric hand mixer to ensure the powder is evenly dispersed throughout the water and to prevent lumps forming.

3. Push the gel through a strainer to ensure a smooth consistency. Add more water if a thinner consistency is desired.

Up to three per cent essential oil may be added to the gel. One per cent dilution is appropriate in most instances.

Linseed gel

Linseed gel is made by pouring boiling water over the linseeds or simmering the linseeds in water to form a gel which is then strained to remove the seeds.

20gm crushed linseeds
200ml boiling water

1. Pour the boiling water over the crushed linseeds and set aside overnight or simmer until a gel forms.

2. Strain the seeds from the gel and add more water if a thinner consistency is desired.

Emulsions

Many skin care preparations are emulsions. Cleansing milks, cleansing creams, face creams and body lotions are examples of skin care preparations which are emulsions.

What is an Emulsion?

An emulsion is a mixture of **oil** and **water** blended together with an **emulsifier** to form a stable mixture.

When an emulsion is made, two phases (the oil phase and the water phase) are required. In both phases, ingredients used singly or in combination are heated. Once the desired temperature is reached, the products of the two phases are combined to form the emulsion.

Oil phase

The oil phase may include any of the following ingredients:

- cold pressed vegetable oils;
- infused oils;
- cocoa butter;
- shea butter;
- beeswax;
- emulsifying wax;
- honey.

Water phase

The water phase may include any of the following ingredients:

- purified, distilled or spring water;
- floral waters;
- infusions and decoctions;
- glycerin;
- borax, if used, should be dissolved into the water phase.

Types of Emulsions

There are two basic types of emulsion, 'oil-in-water' emulsions and 'water-in-oil' emulsions.

Oil-in-water emulsions

- Contain mostly water and a small amount of oil.
- Feel moist on the skin but not greasy.
- Include cleansing milks, face and body lotions, face and body creams.

Water-in-oil emulsions

- Contain mostly oil and a small amount of water.
- Have an oilier, thicker feeling on the skin.
- Include cold creams, ointments, barrier creams.

Basic Ingredients

Emulsifiers

The emulsifier is the ingredient which holds the oil and water together in a stable homogenous emulsion. It is both hydrophilic (attracts water) and lipophilic (attracts oil and fat). The ratio of oil to water in an emulsion determines your choice of emulsifier as certain emulsifiers work better if there is more oil in a formula and others work better if there is more water.

Beeswax and borax

The sodium tetraborate of the borax combines with the cerotic acid of the beeswax to form sodium cerotate, a kind of 'soap', which acts as an emulsifier. This emulsification system works well in water-in-oil type emulsions where the ratio of water to oil is small. The more borax used, the stiffer the preparation will be.

Lecithin

Lecithin may be used as an emulsifier in water-in-oil type emulsions. It is a weaker emulsifier which means your emulsion is more likely to break apart. It is best used in conjunction with another emulsifier. It has skin conditioning properties which makes it a desirable substance to use in skin care preparations.

Emulsifying wax

There are many emulsifying waxes from which to choose. However, those discussed here are plant derived, are generally readily available and serve most general emulsification purposes. They are glyceryl monostearate, cetearyl alcohol, cetyl alcohol, cetearyl polyglucoside and stearic acid. They are used either individually or in combination. Ceteareth 30 is also commonly used. It is a semi-synthetic emulsifier.

As these emulsifiers may be derived from plant (palm or coconut oil) or petrochemical sources it is important to state that you are wishing to purchase a plant-derived or naturally derived emulsifier. It may be easier to tell your supplier the purpose for which you will be using the emulsifying wax to ensure you will be given the correct one.

Preservatives

Preservatives are used in skin and hair care preparations to reduce their deterioration resulting from the action of micro-organisms. Anti-oxidants reduce the oxidation and rancidity of vegetable oils contained in products.

There are a number of factors which need to be considered when seeking to prolong the shelf life of your skin and hair care preparations besides the addition of preservatives.

- Fresh fruits, vegetables and herbs used in preparations will contribute to rapid deterioration. Preparations using fresh fruits, vegetables and herbs should be used immediately or stored in the refrigerator and used within several days.

- Preparations made with dry plant ingredients such as flours, starches and granules will keep well if stored in sealed containers away from light. They may be prone to weevil and insect infestation and granules made from seeds and kernels may become rancid after some time if not kept cool.

- Any preparations containing vegetable oils will oxidise and become rancid after some time. Rancidity will happen more quickly if the preparation is not stored in a sealed container, away from light and heat. Anti-oxidants, such as vitamin E, are often added to preparations containing vegetable oils to reduce oxidation and rancidity.

- Having clean equipment and storage containers will reduce contamination of your preparations and thus deterioration.

- A product is easily contaminated with bacteria from your fingers. A pump action bottle or bottle which can be poured from will reduce contamination and deterioration. If storage of a preparation in a jar is necessary, due to the viscosity of a product not allowing the product to be pumped or poured, use a clean spatula or cotton bud to remove your preparation.

- Any moisture in a product will provide a suitable medium in which bacteria and fungi can grow.

Anti-microbials

Anti-microbial preservatives reduce the growth of bacteria and fungi in your preparations.

Alcohol/ethanol

Ethanol may be used in cosmetic preparations as a preservative at concentrations of 15 to 20 per cent. Pure ethanol is not available for sale to the general public (a licence is needed), but vodka or a perfume alcohol base (which will be the closest to pure ethanol) can be used instead. As vodka has a lower alcohol concentration, more will need to be used in a preparation to take advantage of its preservative properties.

Herbal tinctures, fragrant waters and perfumes often contain alcohol which acts as a solvent as well as a preservative.

To reduce the drying effect of alcohol, glycerol (glycerin) or vegetable oils can be included in a formulation where appropriate.

Tinctures and perfumes made using alcohol can have glycerol added to them to reduce the drying effect of alcohol.

Essential oils

Essential oils which are incorporated into cosmetic preparations will have a mild anti-microbial and thus preservative effect. This effect will vary from oil to oil and as the amount usually incoporated into preparations is relatively low, essential oils will not be effective preservatives by themselves.

Benzoin

Benzoin tincture is often recommended for use as a preservative in homemade cosmetic preparations. Nerys Purchon, author of *Bodycraft*, suggests using a concentration of four per cent benzoin tincture combined with ten per cent glycerin of your total preparation as a preservative.

Powdered benzoin is used to prevent soaps containing fruits and vegetables from spoiling.

Citrus seed extract

Citrus seed extract is an effective natural preservative. It is used in relatively low concentrations. Up to one per cent citrus seed extract is included in preparations such as creams and lotions. It is added to the water phase of a preparation.

Anti-oxidants

Anti-oxidants are used in preparations to prevent vegetable oils from going rancid. A commonly available anti-oxidant is vitamin E.

Pure vitamin E is used in concentrations of up to one per cent of the vegetable oil content. Jojoba oil is a particularly stable oil and does not require anti-oxidants as do other vegetable oils. Other anti-oxidants include vitamins A and C.

Making an Emulsion

Use these instructions to make any of the emulsion preparations listed throughout this book. The ingredients in each recipe will be listed as either 'oil phase' ingredients or 'water phase' ingredients to ensure your ingredients are mixed together correctly.

It is important when heating the ingredients that the correct temperature is reached as separation occurs easily if the ingredients are not hot enough.

1. Weigh out your ingredients.

2. Place the waxes and other solid fats which you may be incorporating into your emulsion into a pyrex jug.

3. Pour your water phase ingredients into another pyrex jug.

4. Place the jugs into a large saucepan or frypan partly filled with water. The jugs should sit on a metal vegetable steamer or egg rings inside the saucepan so that they are not sitting directly on the bottom of the saucepan or frypan. This ensures that the ingredients will not overheat.

5. Place the saucepan onto the stove or turn on the frypan.

6. Add your vegetable oils to the melted waxes and fats and heat until the oil phase reaches 65-70°C.

7. If your recipe requires any vegetable oils which are high in essential fatty acids such as evening primrose oil, rosehip oil, or linseed oil, add them now to your other vegetable oils which you have already heated to 65-70°C. They are not heated with the other vegetable oils as they deteriorate if exposed to high temperatures for too long.

8. Now that both the water phase and oil phase have reached 65-70°C, slowly pour the water phase into the oil phase whilst keeping the oil phase jug sitting in the saucepan in the hot water. Stir continuously while doing this.

9. Once all the water phase ingredients have been incorporated into the oil phase ones remove from the heat. The emulsion will be very watery in consistency and look milky.

10. Continue stirring. If the emulsion is an oil-in-water emulsion, ie contains more water than oil, stir quickly to ensure separation does not occur and consider using an electric stirrer for a short time, approximately 20-30 seconds. (Using an electric stirrer for too long, whips too much air into the emulsion.) If the emulsion is a water-in-oil emulsion, ie contains more oil than water, stir slowly and steadily so that air bubbles are not incorporated, as this may cause the emulsion to separate. Run your spoon regularly over the bottom of the jug ensuring the proper homogenisation of all ingredients.

11. When the emulsion cools to 45°C add your essential oils and stir in thoroughly.

12. Once the emulsion begins to thicken, but is still pourable, pour into jars.

13. Cap and label your jars once the emulsion is cool. Include on your label the purpose of the emulsion, ingredients, and date.

Base cream

This is an all purpose base cream to which you can add pure essential oils, infused oils, cold pressed vegetable oils, floral waters, herbal infusions, and herbal tinctures.

Oil phase

10gm plant-derived emulsifying wax
30ml sweet almond oil

Water phase

5ml vegetable glycerin
150ml purified water
2ml citrus seed extract

To make your base cream follow the directions for making an emulsion on the previous page.

plant soothing clay healing her
aring leaf purifying seed calmin
eauty skin exfoliating relaxing nu
leansing flower moisture mask bu
alm petal gel refreshing massag
alt bath aromatherapy breathin
ruit wellness roots tincture vitamin
nfusion balance harmony honey fee
ash plant soothing clay healin
erb caring leaf purifying see
alming beauty skin exfoliatin
elaxing nut cleansing flowe
oisture mask bud balm petal ge
efreshing massage salt bat
romatherapy breathing fru
ellness roots tincture vitamin
fusion balance bloom create spi

FACE

- **Skin Types and Conditions**
- **Cleansers**
- **Toners**
- **Moisturisers**
- **Facial Treatment Oils**
- **Lip Balms**
- **Eye Creams and Eye Gels**
- **Facial Steaming**
- **Masks**
- **Scrubs and Exfoliants**

Skin Types and Conditions

Proper diagnosis of your skin type and its condition are the keys to identifying the skin care preparations most suitable for your skin. While your skin type is dependent on your genetic make up, many skin conditions may be the result of your treatment of yourself and your skin over the years.

Skin Types

Normal skin

Normal skin looks soft, moist, plump, and dewy and has a healthy glow and colour. The surface of the skin shows a fine texture, and there are no visible wrinkles, fine lines, or open pores.

Dry skin

Dry skin is the result of sebaceous gland underactivity. It is hereditary but can also result from the aging process. Dry skin also tends to be dehydrated. Its lack of oil diminishes its ability to retain moisture. It tends to be very fine, with almost invisible pores and tends to wrinkle easily.

Oily skin

Oily skin is a hereditary condition that develops due to overactive sebaceous glands. This activity is controlled by the androgen hormones. Oily skin can be recognised by its shiny appearance with enlarged pores.

Combination skin

Combination skin is characterised by the existence of two or more different skin types or conditions. A classic combination skin is oily around the nose, forehead, and chin, but dry on the rest of the face.

When treating a combination skin, each area is treated for its particular needs. For example, when applying a mask, a mask formulated for oily skin is applied to the oily areas of the face and a mask formulated for dry skin is applied to dry areas.

Skin Conditions

Skin conditions develop over time and can apply to all four skin types (except acne which is not usually found with dry skin). This means that many combinations of skin are possible, making everyone's skin unique. The most common skin conditions are dehydration, couperose, sensitivity, aging and acne.

Dehydration

This is one of the most common skin conditions. It indicates a lack of sufficient moisture in the cells and intercellular channels.

Dehydration may be caused and aggravated by excessive perspiration, lack of sufficient sebum to prevent evaporation of natural moisture, poor metabolism, and/or insufficient water intake, drinking tea, coffee or soft drinks, taking diuretics, atmospheric conditions, including too much sun and wind and a lack of moisture in the air, air-conditioning, not using moisturisers, and cleansing with harsh soaps and water. Both dry and oily skins can be dehydrated.

Mature skin

The skin loses its elasticity, becomes flaccid and sags, becomes thinner and drier, and shows deepening lines and wrinkles. The skin looks withered and dull. Growths and pigmentation appear along with small capillaries. This all happens in varying degrees as we age.

Sensitivity

A sensitive skin reaction can express itself as redness, itching, burning, and, in the worst cases, as small papules sometimes filled with a watery fluid.

Skin sensitivity is aggravated by certain skin care product ingredients such as perfume and even some essential oils. Facial scrubbing, and the use of astringents with a high level of alcohol, will aggravate this skin condition. Environmental influences such as wind, sun and heat can aggravate sensitive skins.

Acne

Acne is a chronic inflammatory disease of the sebaceous gland and hair follicle. It is characterised by comedones, closed (whiteheads) and open (blackheads), papules, pustules and cysts.

Acne vulgaris is very common during the teenage years. Most adolescents have some manifestation of acne. The peak incidence is in mid-teens in girls and late teens in boys.

In the vast majority of people, acne is a mild and short-lived condition. Most of those with acne are free of the condition by their early twenties. In a few, it persists into the thirties and forties. Premenstrual flares of acne may persist until menopause.

Couperose

Couperose appears as small, dilated, winding, bright red blood vessels on the cheeks, around the nose and sometimes on the chin. It occurs as a result of poor elasticity of the capillary wall and gives the appearance of diffuse or local redness. It is most obvious on fair skin.

Couperose is aggravated by extremes of temperature, by the use of excessively cold or hot water, nervous disorders, digestive disorders, poor nutrition, saunas, exercise that causes the face to turn very red, drinking very hot liquids, eating spicy foods, blushing, smoking, alcohol, harsh and aggressive use of products, such as scrubs, and alcohol-based toners.

Devitalised skin

Devitalised skin takes on a yellowish, dull caste. It is common in Mediterrranean skin types. This type of skin can handle a lot of massage and stimulation to increase blood circulation. If not looked after it can become very tired looking.

Cleansers

The most important part of caring for your skin is cleansing it thoroughly. Without thorough cleansing, the skin can look dull and various skin conditions may develop or be made worse. If you are in perfect health and living in an idyllic, stress-free, pollution-free environment, with balanced climatic conditions, perhaps a rinse with warm water is sufficient.

A cleanser will remove excess oil, perspiration, dirt, dust, pollution, make-up, naturally loosened dead skin cells from the surface of your skin and, to a certain extent, from your skin's pores.

It will help to dislodge blockages, such as blackheads, and can begin to treat a skin problem (for example, rehydrating a dry skin or reducing excess sebum in the case of an oily skin).

Your cleanser should not cause the removal of too much oil or moisture or upset your skin's pH balance significantly. It should not be irritating.

A cleanser is formulated from a choice of the following basic ingredients:

- **water** for moisture and fluidity and to allow it to be rinsed off or removed easily;

- **emollients**, such as vegetable oils, to soften and lubricate the skin and to help dissolve impurities;

- **emulsifiers** to hold together any water and oily components which have been mixed together. (Cleansers usually contain more emulsifier than moisturisers as a larger quantity of emulsifier will help to lift impurities from the skin.);

- **surfactants** to cause foaming and help dissolve and lift impurities from the skin;

- **active ingredients** to help treat a particular skin type or condition. (When adding essential oils and herbal extracts these should be chosen to suit the particular skin type on which the preparation will be used. However, as a cleansing preparation remains on the skin a short time only, a minimal effect will be achieved. As this is the case, keep your choice of active ingredients relatively basic and save your more expensive ingredients for preparations which will remain on the skin.);

- **preservatives** to reduce rapid product deterioration.

Use your cleanser twice daily, in the morning and at the end of the day. Your skin should be cleansed in the morning because your skin excretes waste onto the surface throughout the night. At the end of the day, your skin should be cleansed twice. Once to remove surface impurities, such as pollutants and make-up, and again to better cleanse the pores.

Massage your cleanser thoroughly over your entire face especially over any areas of blocked pores. Then remove it completely with a damp sponge or cloth, and rinse. Your skin will feel clean, soft and hydrated. Follow with a skin toner.

Cleansing Creams

Skins which are dry, dehydrated or sensitive benefit most from cleansing creams and lotions. The removal of make-up is most effectively achieved with a cleansing cream or lotion. Cleansing creams range from thick, oily creams to light, water-soluble creams. Your choice of cleanser will depend on your skin's needs.

Cold cream

A cold cream is a very rich water-in-oil emulsion containing a large amount of oil and a relatively small amount of water. When applied to the skin, the water quickly evaporates causing a cooling effect hence the name 'cold' cream. This emulsion separates easily which allows this to happen. The oil left on the skin mixes with and dissolves impurities on the skin. The oil with dissolved impurities is then removed with warm water and a cleansing sponge or cloth.

It was in the second century AD that the Greek physician, Galen made a crude cream by mixing water into a blend of molten beeswax and olive oil — the first cold cream. By the late nineteenth century, borax was used to stabilise it.

Cold creams are useful for make-up removal and are suitable cleansers for particularly dry skins. The same cream can also be used as a rich moisturiser.

Galen's original cold cream
Skin type: dry

Oil phase
56 parts olive oil

Water phase
24 parts beeswax
20 parts water

Make Galen's cold cream by following the directions for making an emulsion on page 36.

If you would like to make Galen's cold cream, it is important to hand-stir the ingredients and not allow the temperature to drop quickly as separation of ingredients can occur easily.

Rich cleansing cream
Skin type: dry and sensitive

This thick oily cream is based on an early cold cream forumula. It is suitable for make-up removal and for cleansing dry skin.

Oil phase
60ml sweet almond oil
10gm plant-derived emulsifying wax

Water phase
20ml purified water
1ml (20 drops) citrus seed extract

Add at 45°C
10 drops pure essential oil

1. Choose a pure essential oil or essential oil composition for your skin type. See page 23.

2. Make this rich cleansing cream by following the directions for making an emulsion on page 36.

Light cleansing cream
Skin type: normal to dry, sensitive

This cleansing cream is suitable for dry skin and removing make-up. However, it is lighter and easier to remove than the rich cleansing cream.

Oil phase

35ml sweet almond oil
15gm plant-derived emulsifying wax

Water phase

135ml purified water
1ml (20 drops) citrus seed extract

Add at 45°C

1ml (20 drops) pure essential oil

1. Choose a pure essential oil or essential oil composition for your skin type. See page 23.

2. Make this skin-softening cleansing cream by following the directions for making an emulsion on page 36.

Water soluble cleansing cream

Skin type: most skin types

This cleanser is suitable for use on most skin types as it removes impurities without leaving the skin feeling dry. It is lighter than the previous three cleansers and is also suitable for removing make-up. The oil will dissolve the impurities, the emulsifier will allow the oil and impurities to be lifted off the skin and to be mixed with water to be rinsed away.

Oil phase

20ml apricot kernel oil
15gm plant-derived emulsifying wax

Water phase

150ml purified water
1ml (20 drops) citrus seed extract

Add at 45°C

1ml (20 drops) pure essential oil

1. Choose a pure essential oil or essential oil composition for your skin type. See page 23.

2. Make this light cleansing cream by following the directions for making an emulsion on page 36.

Cleansing Oil

As it is the oil in a cleansing cream which helps dissolve the impurities, it is often used on its own in preparations which are used to remove heavy, oil-based make-up or waterproof mascara. An oil cleanser is most suitable for very dry skins which are lacking in oil and for delicate, sensitive skins.

A cleansing oil can be used by massaging the oil over your face and then removing it by gently wiping your face with a face cloth or cotton wool pads and warm water. It may also be used by applying the cleansing oil to a cotton wool pad, which has been dampened with warm water, then wiping this over your face. This method is easier and faster.

Jojoba oil is a superb choice as it has a particularly fine texture. Otherwise, apricot kernel or sweet almond oils, which have a slightly heavier texture, are good choices.

Foaming Cleansers

This type of cleanser is particularly suitable for oilier skins as no oil is left behind to exacerbate this kind of condition. Foaming cleansers can be modified by varying the quantity and type of foaming agent (surfactant) used in the formula and by the addition of other ingredients, such as vegetable oils.

The following foaming cleansers are based on Castile liquid soap, a very gentle skin cleanser, which is based on olive oil.

Castile liquid soap

Castile liquid soap may be used to cleanse oily skins. Only a small quantity needs to be used. Massage it over a damp face and remove by rinsing or removing with a damp face cloth or sponge. The addition of the appropriate pure essential oils will help to improve your skin's condition.

Castile cleansing wash

Skin type: normal to oily

100ml Castile liquid soap
20 drops pure essential oil

1. Choose a pure essential oil or essential oil composition from page 23 and add to the Castile liquid soap.

2. Shake the ingredients together and store in a clean bottle.

Gentle almond and Castile cleanser

Skin type: normal to dry

A mild cleansing wash for dry skins may be made by adding a small quantity of vegetable oil to the Castile liquid soap.

90ml Castile liquid soap
10ml sweet almond oil
20 drops pure essential oil

1. Choose a pure essential oil or essential oil composition for your skin type from page 23 and add to the Castile liquid soap and almond oil blend.

2. Shake all ingredients together and store in a clean bottle.

Soapwort gentle skin cleanser

Skin type: sensitive

A particularly gentle cleansing preparation for sensitive, irritated, and/or inflamed skins.

10gm soapwort root
250ml water

1. Boil and simmer the soapwort root in the water for 30 minutes.

2. Remove from the heat and allow to cool.

3. Strain the liquid and use as it is. Use within a couple of days.

Shaving cream

A shaving cream can be made by mixing a small quantity of soap powder into a cleansing cream formula.

Oil phase

35ml sweet almond oil
15gm plant-derived emulsifying wax

Water phase

125ml purified water
2ml (40 drops) citrus seed extract
20gm soap-based powder or flakes

Add at 45°C

20 drops pure essential oil

1. Choose an essential oil or essential oil composition for your skin type to add to your shaving cream. See page 23.

2. Make this shaving cream by following the directions for making an emulsion on page 36.

3. Add the soap base to the mixture once all ingredients have been emulsified and stir in slowly to ensure it does not foam unnecessarily.

4. Store in a clean jar.

Toners

A toner, also known as a skin freshener or toning lotion, is an aqueous liquid which is used after cleansing.

Toners are used to:

- remove any traces of cleanser still left on the skin as well as any tap water which has been used to rinse the skin;
- help redress the skin's pH balance (The skin does this naturally after a period of time.);
- help treat a skin condition due to the content of active ingredients;
- minimise temporarily pore size (This happens when the skin is either cooled or if it is restored to its slightly acidic pH of 4.5 to 6. This causes the salt-type cross linkages between the molecules of keratin to reform.);
- cool, soothe and refresh the skin.

Use your toner by applying it to damp cotton wool and wiping it over your face or spraying it over your face.

It is the first step in adding moisture to the skin's surface, as it is left on the skin, and is applied to the skin just before the application of a moisturiser. Do not allow your skin to dry out completely before applying your moisturiser.

Formulate your own toner by using the following active plant ingredients.

Floral waters

Distilled floral or herb waters used by themselves or in combination with other ingredients make excellent healing and soothing toning lotions. Refer to page 16 to choose a floral water which is suitable for your skin type.

Herbal infusions

Herbal infusions which have been allowed to cool can be used as healing toning lotions. Refer to the section starting at page 8 to choose herbs which are suitable for your skin type.

Aloe vera juice can be used on its own, for its soothing, healing benefits, or added as an ingredient to floral and herb waters or infusions.

Herbal vinegars

Herbal vinegars make excellent skin toners. The apple cider vinegar helps redress the skin's pH and the herbs add other healing properties.

Make a herbal vinegar by following the directions on page 26.

To make a skin toner, dilute one teaspoon of the herbal vinegar in 100ml of purified water, floral water or herbal infusion. A herbal vinegar skin tonic made with purified water or floral water will keep much longer than one made with a herbal infusion and can be stored in a clean bottle.

Honey water

Skin type: oily and blemished

A healing astringent toner for oily and blemished skin.

**5ml (1 tsp) honey
100ml purified water
5ml (1 tsp) apple cider vinegar
2-3 drops bergamot essential oil**

1. Dissolve the honey in warm water.

2. Add the bergamot essential oil to the apple cider vinegar and add this to the honey water.

3. Store in a clean bottle and keep in the fridge.

Witch-hazel skin soother

Skin type: oily and blemished

A soothing, healing toner for oily and blemished skin.

**45ml witch-hazel water
5ml (1 tsp) aloe vera juice
5 drops citrus seed extract**

1. Thoroughly mix the ingredients.

2. Store in a clean bottle and keep in the fridge.

Lemon freshener

Skin type: oily and blemished

An astringent and antiseptic skin toner for oily and blemished skin.

**5ml (1 tsp) lemon juice
50ml purified water**

1. Mix both ingredients.

2. Store in a clean container and keep in the fridge. Use within three or four days.

Chilled cucumber tonic

Skin type: normal, combination and sensitive

A cool, refreshing skin toner for sensitive, combination and normal skin.

1/3 cucumber (peeled)

1. Juice the cucumber and strain it.

2. Store in a clean container and keep in the fridge. Use within three or four days.

Lavender and myrrh healing toner

Skin type: oily and blemished

A healing, antiseptic and gentle astringent for oily and blemished skin.

**1.5ml (30 drops) myrrh tincture
100ml lavender water**

Mix both ingredients and store in a clean bottle.

Gentle rose tonic

Skin type: sensitive

A calming, soothing skin freshener for sensitive and irritated skins.

**85ml rosewater
15ml aloe vera juice
10 drops essential oil solubiliser
2 drops blue chamomile essential oil**

1. Mix the chamomile essential oil and the essential oil solubiliser.

2. Add to that mixture the rosewater and aloe vera juice.

3. Place the mixture in a clean bottle, shake well and store in the fridge.

Chamomile and calendula soothing mist

Skin type: sensitive

Another calming, soothing skin freshener for sensitive and irritated skins.

1. Make a chamomile and calendula infusion by following the instructions on page 24.

2. Pour the infusion into a spray bottle and mist over your face or apply to cotton wool pads and wipe over your face. As this toner is an infusion, it must be stored in the fridge and used within two or three days.

Flower and juice skin toner

Skin type: sensitive and combination

A very soothing and cooling skin toner for sensitive and combination skins.

**80ml orange flower water
20ml aloe vera juice**

1. Mix both ingredients.

2. Store in a clean bottle and keep in the fridge.

Sandalwood hydrating toner

Skin type: dehydrated

A wonderfully hydrating and calming toner for dehydrated skins.

**1ml (20 drops) essential oil solubiliser
10 drops sandalwood essential oil
100ml rosewater**

1. Add the sandalwood essential oil to the essential oil solubiliser.

2. Add the rosewater to this mixture.

3. Shake the mixture to disperse the ingredients properly.

4. Store in a clean bottle.

Pure rose skin liquid

Skin type: dry and mature

A beautiful fragrant and gently hydrating skin tonic for dry and mature skins.

**100ml rosewater
5 drops rose absolute
10 drops essential oil solubiliser**

1. Add the rose absolute to the essential oil solubiliser.

2. Add the rosewater to this mixture.

3. Shake the mixture to disperse the ingredients properly.

4. Store in a clean bottle.

Aromatic facial mist

Wonderfully refreshing, a great mist to keep cool in a refrigerator in summer. Imagine misting yourself with rose or sandalwood or neroli.

Suitable for all skin types.

**100ml purified water or floral water
1ml (20 drops) pure essential oil or essential oil composition
2ml (40 drops) essential oil solubiliser**

1. Add your chosen essential oil or essential oil composition to the essential oil solubiliser.

2. Add the water or floral water to this mixture.

3. Shake the mixture to disperse the ingredients properly.

4. Store in a clean bottle.

Moisturisers

A moisturiser, as the name implies, will provide moisture to the surface layers of the skin and will prevent dehydration and dryness. It keeps your skin smooth and supple.

A moisturiser will be formulated from a selection of the following ingredients:

- **water** to add moisture to your skin and fluidity to your moisturiser (Choose from distilled water, purified water, bottled water or floral waters for the water component of your skin moisturisers. Moisturisers for oilier skin types will tend to have a much higher water content than moisturisers for drier skins.);

- **emollients** to soften and lubricate the skin and prevent moisture/water evaporation (Cold pressed vegetable oils and natural plant butters, such as cocoa butter and shea butter, have these properties. Moisturisers for drier skin types will have a much higher emollient content than moisturisers for oilier skins.);

- **emulsifiers** to hold together any water and oil components in the form of a cream or lotion;

- **waxes** to make the product firm and, depending on the quantity used, may provide a slight barrier effect;

- **humectants** to bind water (They hold moisture in your cream and onto your skin. Vegetable glycerin is often used for this purpose.);

- **active ingredients** are chosen to help treat a particular skin type or condition (These include essential oils and herbal extracts.);

- **preservatives** to reduce deterioration due to the action of micro-organisms.

A moisturiser is applied after toning and before make-up application and massaged into the skin with firm upward strokes and then pressed into the skin.

A selection of moisturising creams follows. Once you feel confident with your cream-making skills you may like to substitute vegetable oils, infused oils, floral waters and pure essential oils, for other ingredients of the same type to create new recipes.

When using the creams on your face, remove them from the jars with a spatula or cotton tip to avoid contaminating them with bacteria.

Cocoa butter rich moisture cream
Skin type: very dry

A rich nourishing and moisturising cream for very dry skin. It may also be used as a night cream.

Oil phase

20ml (1 tbsp) avocado oil
5gm cocoa butter
8gm plant-derived emulsifying wax
5ml (1 tsp) vitamin E oil

Water phase

55ml purified water
5ml (1 tsp) vegetable glycerin
1ml (20 drops) citrus seed extract

Add at 45°C

**1ml (20 drops) sandalwood essential oil
or dry skin composition** (see page 23)

Make the cocoa butter rich moisture cream by following the intructions for making an emulsion on page 36.

Lavender face cream

Skin type: dry and sensitive

A soothing, refreshing and fragrant moisturising cream for dry and sensitive skin.

Oil phase

**80ml (4 tbsp) sweet almond oil
10gm cocoa butter
10gm plant-derived emulsifying wax**

Water phase

**80ml (4 tbsp) lavender water
1ml (20 drops) citrus seed extract**

Add at 45°C

**15 drops lavender essential oil or
sensitive skin composition** (see page 23)

Make the lavender face cream by following the instructions for making an emulsion on page 36.

Rosehip vital essence cream

Skin type: dry and mature

A rich, nourishing moisturising cream for mature skin which has become dry, damaged and lacking in tone.

Oil phase

**20ml (1 tbsp) apricot kernel oil
5gm shea butter
5ml (1 tsp) carrot infused oil
5ml (1 tsp) evening primrose oil
5ml (1 tsp) rosehip oil
8gm plant-derived emulsifying wax
5ml (1 tsp) vitamin E oil**

Water phase

**50ml (2½ tbsp) rosewater
5ml (1 tsp) vegetable glycerin
1ml (20 drops) citrus seed extract**

Add at 45°C

**1ml (20 drops) frankincense essential oil
or mature skin composition** (see page 23)

Make the rosehip vital essence cream by following the instructions for making an emulsion on page 36.

Add the evening primrose oil and rosehip oil, which are very heat sensitive, to the oil phase just as it reaches the correct temperature in order that they are not exposed to a high temperature for any length of time.

Pure plant moisture cream

Skin type: normal

This cream is suitable for normal skin, that is skin which is relatively balanced in its oil and moisture content. It will help to maintain the skin and protect it from dryness.

Oil phase

**30ml apricot kernel oil
20ml jojoba oil
8gm plant-derived emulsifying wax**

Water phase

**70ml purified water
5ml vegetable glycerin
1ml (20 drops) citrus seed extract**

Add at 45°C

**1ml (20 drops) ylang ylang essential oil
or normal skin composition** (see page 23)

Make the pure plant moisture cream by following the instructions for making an emulsion on page 36.

Jojoba fine moisture cream
Skin type: combination

A beautiful cream for skins requiring a lighter moisturiser. Combination skin, and skin which is both oily and dehydrated, will benefit from using this cream.

Oil phase

12ml jojoba oil
8gm plant-derived emulsifying wax

Water phase

75ml purified water
5ml (1 tsp) vegetable glycerin
1ml (20 drops) citrus seed extract

Add at 45°C

1ml (20 drops) geranium essential oil or combination skin composition
(see page 23)

Make the jojoba fine moisture cream by following the instructions for making an emulsion on page 36.

Rare roses moisture cream
Skin type: most skin types

The feel and smell of preparations containing pure rose extracts are a divine treat for the skin and soul. The rare roses moisture cream is a beautiful, light moisture cream for most skin types, except for very oily skins.

Oil phase

15ml sweet almond oil
8gm plant-derived emulsifying wax

Water phase

70ml rosewater
5ml (1 tsp) vegetable glycerin
1ml (1 tsp) citrus seed extract

Add at 45°C

10 drops rose absolute or rose otto

Make the rare roses moisture cream by following the instructions for making an emulsion on page 36.

Calendula caring cream
Skin type: sensitive

A wonderfully soothing and healing cream for sensitive skins including skins with eczema, psoriasis and dermatitis.

Oil phase

25ml calendula infused oil
8gm plant-derived emulsifying wax

Water phase

65ml purified water
5ml (1 tsp) vegetable glycerin
1ml (20 drops) citrus seed extract

Add at 45°C

10 drops sensitive skin composition
(see page 23)

Make the calendula caring cream by following the instructions for making an emulsion on page 36.

Skin-regulating moisture gel
Skin type: oily

A great oil-free moisturiser for very oily skins which block at the mere sight of any products containing oil.

2gm xanthan gum
100ml purified water (or floral water)
5ml (1 tsp) vegetable glycerin
5 drops lemon essential oil
2 drops geranium essential oil
2 drops juniper essential oil

Make the skin-regulating moisture gel by following the instructions for making a gel on page 31.

Blemish gel

This gel is an antiseptic healing gel for pimples and spots. It should only be applied directly to the pimple or spot, not all over the face, as the concentration of essential oils is relatively high.

2gm xanthan gum
100ml lavender water
10 drops tea tree essential oil
20 drops lemon essential oil
25 drops lavender essential oil

Make the blemish gel by following the instructions for making a gel on page 31.

'Pick-me-up' gel

A great pick-me-up gel which may be used to cool and refresh all skin types. It may be applied before putting on your regular moisturiser or throughout the day whenever you need a pick-me-up!

2gm xanthan gum
100ml rosewater
5ml (1 tsp) vegetable glycerin
11 drops lemon essential oil
4 drops ylang ylang essential oil

Make this gel by following the instructions for making a gel on page 31.

Facial Treatment Oils

Facial treatment oils are usually a combination of cold-pressed vegetable oils, infused oils and pure essential oils.

Facial treatment oils may be applied to your skin by themselves or used under a moisturiser. You may prefer to use them at night instead of a night cream or under a night cream. They may also be used in a facial as a treatment massage oil.

To make a personalised facial treatment oil, choose suitable cold-pressed vegetable oils and pure essential oils for your skin type. Follow the directions for blending and diluting essential oils on page 19.

The following blends make superb facial treatment oils.

Dry skin treatment oil

15ml avocado oil
10ml wheatgerm oil
15ml evening primrose oil
10ml carrot infused oil
3 drops rose absolute
3 drops palmarosa essential oil
4 drops rosewood essential oil

Dehydrated skin treatment oil

30ml apricot kernel oil
20ml jojoba oil
5 drops sandalwood essential oil
3 drops lavender essential oil
2 drops ylang ylang essential oil

Mature skin treatment oil

20ml rosehip oil
25ml apricot kernel oil
5ml carrot infused oil
3 drops frankincense essential oil
6 drops rose absolute
1 drop patchouli essential oil

Scar treatment oil

20ml wheatgerm oil
10ml rosehip oil
10ml calendula infused oil
10ml hypericum infused oil
4 drops lavender essential oil
3 drops patchouli essential oil
3 drops frankincense essential oil

Combination skin treatment oil

25ml jojoba oil
25ml apricot kernel oil
3 drops grapefruit essential oil
2 drops petitgrain essential oil
2 drops geranium essential oil
2 drops patchouli essential oil

Oily skin treatment oil

50ml jojoba oil
6 drops lemon essential oil
2 drops geranium essential oil
2 drops juniper essential oil

Sensitive skin treatment oil

25ml apricot kernel oil
25ml calendula infused oil
3 drops blue chamomile essential oil
2 drops everlasting essential oil

Devitalised skin treatment oil

30ml apricot kernel oil
10ml wheatgerm oil
10ml carrot infused oil
3 drops rosemary essential oil
5 drops lemongrass essential oil
2 drops vetiver essential oil

Broken capillary/couperose treatment oil

25ml calendula infused oil
3 drops cypress essential oil
2 drops blue chamomile essential oil
2 drops geranium essential oil

Pimple treatment oil

Apply pure lavender or tea tree essential oil,
with a cotton bud, directly to a pimple three
times a day.

Lip Balms

Lip balms soften and protect the skin on your lips. Natural lip balms are made from vegetable oils, waxes and fats rather than petro-chemicals such as petrolatum and mineral oils.

Pure essential oils may be added to your lip balm to add delicious flavours or to add healing and antiseptic properties. A maximum dilution of one per cent of essential oil may be added to your lip balm (20 drops to every 100gm of lip balm). Essential oils chosen should be safe to use on sensitive skin, such as the lips. They should be non-toxic, and they should not photosensitise the skin.

Choose from the following essential oils to add to your lip balm:

> aniseed, lime, mandarin,
> myrrh, orange, peppermint,
> sandalwood, and spearmint.

Include healing infused oils such as calendula, carrot and hypericum in your lip balm.

Making a lip balm

1. Melt the beeswax and cocoa butter in a bain-marie.

2. Add the vegetable oils and glycerin or honey, keeping the mixture over the heat.

3. Once the mixture is liquid, remove it from the heat.

4. Using an electric hand mixer, stir the mixture to ensure the honey and glycerin are well dispersed in the mixture and do not sink to the bottom.

5. Once the mixture begins to cool, stir in the essential oils.

6. Pour into small jars.

Fat chocolate lip balm

For lovers of sweets and chocolates. Smells and tastes wonderful.

15gm beeswax
5gm cocoa butter
5gm honey
65ml jojoba oil
10ml natural vanilla essence

Healing lip balm

This lip balm is wonderful for healing dry, cracked, sore lips.

15gm beeswax
5gm cocoa butter
5gm honey
65ml jojoba oil
5ml carrot infused oil
5ml calendula infused oil
3 drops sandalwood essential oil
2 drops myrrh essential oil

Luscious lime lip balm

A delicious, fun, natural lip balm for keeping your lips soft and moisturised.

10gm (2 tsp) beeswax
5gm (1 tsp) cocoa butter
80ml (4 tbsp) sweet almond oil
5ml (1 tsp) vegetable glycerin
20 drops distilled lime essential oil

Creamy honey lip balm

½ tsp honey
12gm shea butter

Pure shea butter may be used as a softening lip balm by itself. To give it a delicious taste, stir a tiny amount of honey into the shea butter. It will be tempting to lick your lips. You may have to melt the shea butter first, then stir in the honey.

Cold sore healing preparation

Some of us are prone to cold sores as we have, at some time, been infected with the *Herpes simplex* virus.

When we are under stress and our immune systems are low, a cold sore will rear its ugly head.

Pure melissa essential oil applied neat to the cold sore at regular intervals throughout the day will help clear it quickly. However, as it is a very expensive essential oil you may like to use the following formula.

15 drops tea tree essential oil
10 drops geranium essential oil
3 drops thyme essential oil
25ml myrrh tincture

1. Mix the essential oils into into the myrrh tincture in a clean bottle.

2. Apply the preparation to the cold sore at regular intervals throughout the day.

Eye Creams and Eye Gels

The skin around the eyes is very thin and has fewer oil glands than the rest of the face. It is also wrinkled up and stretched out may times during our day, as we talk and express ourselves, squint to protect our eyes from the sun and bright lights, and blink to keep our eyes lubricated.

It is important to keep the skin around the eyes moisturised and protected but without weighing it down with heavy creams.

Light eye cream

This is a light moisturising cream for the skin around the eyes. It is suitable for most skin types including sensitive.

Oil phase

15ml apricot kernel oil
10ml calendula infused oil
8gm plant-derived emulsifying wax

Water phase

70ml purified water
5ml (1 tsp) vegetable glycerin
1ml (1 tsp) citrus seed extract

Make this light moisturising eye cream by following the directions for making an emulsion on page 36.

Nourishing eye cream

This eye cream is a rich moisturiser for dry, wrinkled skin around the eyes. Use sparingly.

Oil phase

25ml avocado oil
10ml (2 tsp) carrot infused oil
5ml (1 tsp) wheatgerm oil
5gm (1 tsp) shea butter
8gm plant-derived emulsifying wax

Water phase

50ml (2½ tbsp) rosewater
5ml (1 tsp) vegetable glycerin
1ml (20 drops) citrus seed extract

Make this very nourishing eye cream by following the directions for making an emulsion on page 36.

Revitalising eye gel

This is a soothing, revitalising eye gel for tired and puffy eyes.

2gm xanthan gum
100ml rosewater
5ml (1tsp) vegetable glycerin

Make the revitalising eye gel by following the instructions for making a gel on page 31.

Facial Steaming

Facial steaming benefits your skin in the following ways by:

- increasing perspiration which encourages the removal of wastes and cleanses the sweat pores;
- softening sebum build-up and loosening dead skin cells;
- improving skin hydration.

If you have many clogged pores it is advisable to have a facial steam once a day for two to three days in succession, then two to three times each week. For most skin types once a week, or once a fortnight, is sufficient.

Too much steaming can cause dehydration of the skin. Do not steam your face if you have any broken veins, hypersensitive skin, inflammation, sunburn or if steam adversely affects your breathing.

Herbal steaming

Choose herbs for your skin type from those starting on page 8.

1. Ensure your face has been cleansed and left a little damp.

2. Add two tablespoons of dried herbs or four tablespoons of freshly chopped herbs to two litres of water in a pot. Cover the pot with the lid.

3. Bring the pot to the boil and simmer for about three minutes.

4. Remove the pot from the stove, turn off the heat and remove the lid.

5. Ensuring your hair is kept off your face, cover your head and the pot with a towel, making a tent. Allow the steam to waft onto your face. Keep your face about 30cm or more away from the water, and further if your skin is delicate or has surface veins.

6. Allow the steam to cover your entire face.

7. Steam your face for up to ten minutes.

8. After steaming, wipe over your face with a skin freshener or apply a face mask or rinse your face with the strained, cooled herbal water.

Aromatherapy steaming

Add about five drops of an appropriate essential oil to a bowl of steaming water and follow the directions as for herbal steaming. Choose an essential oil for your skin type from the list starting at page 20.

Facial compresses

A very gentle alternative to steaming is to use a facial compress.

1. Prepare your water and herbs or essential oils in the same way as for facial steaming, but allow the water to cool.

2. While it is still quite warm, dip a cloth into the water and then wring out any excess.

3. Press the cloth over your face. Hold it onto your face for ten seconds or so.

4. Once the cloth feels cool, repeat the procedure. Do this about ten times.

5. Follow with a toner or a mask.

Masks

Use a mask regularly to revitalise your skin.

Masks are used to cleanse the skin, absorb excess oil, remove dead skin cells, soften blackheads, heal damaged or blemished skin, stimulate the circulation in the skin and stimulate healthy cell regeneration, nourish, moisturise, hydrate and soothe your skin and improve skin colour and tone — all depending on the ingredients used to make your mask.

There are two basic types of masks:

- **setting, absorbing masks** (These kinds of masks dry and set on the skin. They are cleansing, drawing, toning and stimulating and may contain healing ingredients. Clays — white, green, pink, red, and yellow; kaolin; Fuller's earth; zinc; sulphur and egg white are commonly used ingredients in these masks.);

- **non-setting, adsorbing masks** (These kinds of masks will infuse active ingredients into the skin, hydrate, soothe and calm, heal and freshen the skin. They tend to remain moist on the skin and may be cream or gel-based or made from plants, fruits, vegetables, herbs, honey or eggs.).

Different types of masks may be applied to your face at the same time to treat different skin types and conditions. For example, your skin may be oily and blocked on your T-zone and on this area you would use a clay mask, whereas your cheeks may be dry and sensitive and here a cream mask may be more suitable.

A mask is usually applied after the skin has been cleansed. If you are giving yourself a facial, use a mask after cleansing, exfoliating and steaming. Leave your face mask on for approximately ten to 15 minutes before removing. Follow with a toner and a moisturiser.

Freshly cooked masks

When you're making your dinner, save some of your cooked vegetables for later. Use them in your face masks to soothe and soften your skin. Potatoes, sweet potatoes, carrots, and pumpkin can be mashed and mixed into a smooth paste with a small amount of vegetable oil and milk. Apply this to your face and leave on for ten to 15 minutes before removing. Great for dry and sensitive skins.

Gel masks

Gel masks are refreshing, cooling and soothing to the skin. Xanthan gum, guar gum, linseeds and pectin can all be used to make your gel masks. Follow the directions on page 31 for making up your gel masks. Gel masks can be made with floral waters or herbal infusions. To make an aromatherapy gel mask, add two drops of essential oil to every 50gm (two tbsp) of gel.

Clay masks

Clay masks are absorbent, cleansing and healing. Clays are available in different colours depending on their mineral content and as a consequence have various healing properties on the skin.

Argiletz clays (green, pink, red, yellow, white), kaolin, Fuller's earth and bentonite are all suitable clays for face masks. See the section on raw ingredients (from page 11) for more information on each of these clays and which ones are suitable for your skin.

Making a clay mask

When making a clay mask, use glass, porcelain or stainless steel utensils (avoid corrosive metals).

To make a clay mask, mix two teaspoons of water with a heaped teaspoon of clay. Floral waters, fruit and vegetable juices, herbal infusions and aloe vera juice may be used in place of water. Mix it into a smooth paste and apply a thin layer to a clean damp face. Leave on for approximately 15 minutes.

If your skin is dry or sensitive do not allow the mask to dry-out on your skin. Spray or sponge the mask with water whenever you feel it beginning to dry. A small amount of vegetable oil may be added to the mask to prevent it from drying out.

Deep cleansing clay mask

Skin type: oily and combination

A cleansing and healing mask for oily, combination and clogged skins.

30gm green clay
50ml orange flower water
5ml vegetable glycerin
10 drops citrus seed extract
1 drop juniper
3 drops lemon

Make this deep cleansing clay mask by mixing the orange flower water into the clay making it into a smooth paste. Then add the other ingredients ensuring the essential oils are mixed thoroughly into the mask.

Fresh from the fridge

Open your fridge door to find the ingredients for a fresh facial mask ready to be made for your skin.

Tahini

To soften and moisturise **dry skin**, spread some tahini over your face and leave on for 10-15 minutes or mix it with a fruit mask.

Fresh fruit and vegetable masks

Strawberries, cucumbers, bananas, grapes, tomatoes, watermelons, apples, citrus fruits and juice, passionfruits, peaches, pears, potatoes, rockmelons, pineapples and paw paws. Whether they're straight from your garden, your local organic food supplier or supermarket, fresh fruit and vegetables make superb face masks. Full of enzymes, vitamins, minerals, sugars, proteins and more. For more detailed information on the properties of each of these fresh fruits and vegetables, and which ones are suitable for your skin, see page 4.

Mash or grate the fruit or vegetable and drain the juice. It can be mixed with a flour (wheat, corn, potato or lentil), clay or xanthan gum, guar gum or pectin into a paste so that the fruit can be easily applied to your face.

Here are a few fresh fruit and vegetable mask recipes for you to get your imagination going. They are all made fresh and in small quantities, enough for one or two applications. They will need to be stored in the fridge and used within four to five days.

Remember to wash your fruit thoroughly before making your masks.

Fruit crush mask

Skin type: oily and blemished

This is a great mask for skins which look a bit dull and have a few pimples. It gently cleanses the skin, the pineapple and paw paw's enzymes dissolve the surface skin cells and the kaolin absorbs impurities.

1 tbsp pineapple
1 tbsp paw paw
2 tbsp kaolin

Mash the pineapple and paw paw together, drain off the juice and mix the pulp into a smooth paste with the kaolin. Apply to a clean face.

Fresh orange face mask

Skin type: oily and blemished

A great cleansing mask for oily, blemished skins.

1 tsp green clay
1½ tsp fresh orange juice

Mix together into a smooth paste and apply to a damp face.

Grape hydration mask

Skin type: all skin types

A cooling, hydrating mask for all skin types.

1 tbsp crushed grape pulp
1 tsp guar gum

Slowly add the guar gum to the crushed grapes, whisking it in as you go. Preferably use an electric hand mixer.

Avocado moisturising mask

Skin type: dry and mature

A moisturising and skin-softening mask for dry and mature skins.

½ ripe avocado
½ tsp avocado oil
2 tbsp thickened cream

Mix the ingredients together into a smooth paste and apply to a damp face.

Cabbage mask

Skin type: blemished

Dip a couple of cabbage leaves into boiling water to soften them. Allow them to cool before applying the leaves to your face. Place them over your face for five to ten minutes. This mask is particularly suitable for skins with pimples.

Cucumber cooling mask

Skin type: sensitive and inflamed

This mask is cooling and soothing to red, irritated skins.

Slice a cool cucumber that has been in the fridge into very thin slices. Apply to a damp face.

Seaweed mask

Skin type: dehydrated

Buy your sheets of toasted seaweed from your local Asian supermarket to make this wonderful healing and softening face mask. A seaweed face mask leaves your skin looking calm and hydrated.

To make this mask, just cut your sheet of seaweed into small squares. Dip the squares into water so that they become slightly soft and paste over a damp face. Leave on for 15-20 minutes. You may want to spray water over the mask during this time if it looks like drying out. When you are ready to remove the mask, peel off the pieces and wipe over your face with a damp face cloth or cleansing sponge.

Oats mask

Skin type: sensitive and inflamed

To soothe irritated and inflamed skins, mix rolled oats into a paste with some yoghurt and smooth over your face.

Healthy herb masks

The number of herbal masks you can make is limited only to what you grow in your garden, or what is available at your greengrocer or herb shops.

Fresh parsley and mint face mask

Skin type: dull and devitalised

Blend a handful of finely chopped parsley and mint together with a tablespoon of yoghurt. Smooth this mask over your face to stimulate a dull, sluggish skin. It is a great pick-me-up for your skin.

Marshmallow and comfrey mask

Skin type: sensitive

This mask is particularly healing and soothing on sensitive skins.

2 tsp marshmallow root
2 tsp comfrey root or leaf
½ cup purified water
½ tsp pectin

Soak the marshmallow root and comfrey in the water overnight. Strain the plant matter from the water the next morning and whisk in the pectin to thicken the mask. Apply to damp skin.

Cream masks

Cream masks are softening and nourishing to the skin. They act as intensive moisturisers for the skin.

Regenerative cream mask

Skin type: dry and mature

This mask is very nourishing to dry and mature skin. It is loaded with beta-carotene and vitamin E. The regenerative cream mask may be applied as a mask first, then any excess massaged into the skin or blotted off with a tissue.

Oil phase

10ml carrot infused oil
30ml avocado oil
10ml wheatgerm oil
8gm plant-derived emulsifying wax

Water phase

50ml rosewater
1ml (20 drops) citrus seed extract

Add at 45°C

1ml (20 drops) patchouli essential oil or mature skin composition (see page 23)

Make the regenerative cream mask by following the instructions for making an emulsion on page 36.

Scrubs and Exfoliants

Scrubs and exfoliants are used to remove dead skin cells from the surface of the skin and to help dislodge clogging of the skin including blackheads and whiteheads.

The removal of surface skin cells and the stimulation of circulation will encourage cellular renewal and allow for the better absorption of active ingredients in masks and moisturisers.

How often you need to exfoliate will depend on the type of peel used and on your skin type. This could be anything from once a fortnight on extremely fine and sensitive skins to up to three times a week on thick, greasy skins and this may be short term only. Overuse and usign preparations with sharp granules, can cause problems such as rough skin due to damage and dehydration of the new cells being formed in the germinative layer of the skin. Skin irritation, disturbance of the skin's pH and broken capillaries can be other adverse effects.

Exfoliants are available in the following forms.

- **Friction Peels**. Friction peels are creamy and are applied to the skin and allowed to dry. The dead skin cells adhere to the peel and it is frictioned off by gentle rubbing with the pads of the fingers whilst supporting the skin. Fine, sensitive and dehydrated skins will benefit from this type of peel.

- **Granular Peels**. Granular peels are creamy substances containing granules which, when massaged over the surface of the skin, mechanically lift the dead skin cells off the surface of the skin and, to a certain extent, cleanse the pores. The granules can be made from ground and polished nuts, seeds, grains and pulses, including almond meal, oatmeal, oat flakes, ground lentils, adzuki beans and rice, semolina, bran and lecithin. This type of peel is of special benefit to oily skins with blocked pores. It can also be quite stimulating.

- **Enzymatic Peels**. Enzymatic peels contain enzymes which dissolve and digest the protein of dead skin cells and help dissolve build-up in pores. Paw paw and pineapple contain natural plant enzymes which have this action.

- **Alpha-hydroxy acids**. Alpha-hydroxy acids (AHAs) occur naturally in fruits such as citrus (citric acid), apples (malic acid) and tomatoes (lactic acid). When AHAs are used in low dilution they act as moisturisers but in higher concentrations they cause skin exfoliation. The AHAs in masks made from fresh fruits are buffered by other constituents such as fruit sugars.

Fresh from the fridge

The following facial scrubs and exfoliants are made fresh. They are delicious and very effective. Make them up in small quantities and store them in the fridge. Use them within four to five days. The following quantities will give you one to two applications.

Gentle fruit acid mask

Skin type: dehydrated with blocked pores

A wonderful skin smoothing and hydrating mask for dehydrated skin with blocked pores.

1 green apple
1 lemon
1 tomato
citrus pectin

1. Juice the green apple, lemon, and tomato.
2. Add enough pectin to form a thick gel.
3. Apply thickly to the face and leave on for 15 to 20 minutes.

Strawberry smoothie

Skin type: oily and sensitive

A gentle scrub for oily and sensitive skins.

1½ tsp oatmeal
1 tsp mashed strawberries

Mix together into a smooth paste and massage over a damp face. Rinse off with warm water.

Almond and avocado soft scrub

Skin type: dry

A skin smoothing exfoliant for dry skin.

1 tsp almond meal
2 tsp mashed avocado

Mix together into a smooth paste and massage over a damp face. Rinse off with warm water.

Creamed rice exfoliant

Skin type: normal to dry

A good cleansing scrub for normal to dry skin.

1 tsp ground rice
2 tsp natural yoghurt or cream

Mix together into a smooth paste and massage over a damp face. Rinse off with warm water.

Paw paw skin scrub

Skin type: all skin types

A scrub with granules and enzymes for most skin types.

1 tsp semolina
2 tsp mashed paw paw

Mix together into a smooth paste and massage over a damp face. Rinse off with warm water.

Banana peel scrub

Skin type: normal to dry, sensitive

A scrumptious scrub for normal to dry and sensitive skins.

2 tsp rolled oats
2 tsp mashed banana
1 tsp honey
1 tsp fresh milk

This face scrub may be applied as a face mask first then massaged over the face and used as a peel. Mix all ingredients into a smooth paste, apply to your face, leave on for ten minutes then massage over your face before removing.

Cinnamon skin polish

Skin type: all skin types

A fragrant skin smoothing scrub for most skin types.

**2 tsp oatmeal
2 tsp dried milk
1 tsp powdered cinnamon**

Just add water to this one. Mix into a smooth paste and massage over a damp face. The dried contents can be stored in a jar ready for use at any time.

Long-life skin scrubs

The following scrubs can be kept for at least six months, if stored out of the heat and kept as uncontaminated as possible.

Pure lavender scrub

Skin type: oily with blocked pores

An excellent scrub for oily skin and skin with blocked pores.

**1 tbsp rice granules or
semolina granules
2 tsp kaolin
1 tsp honey
2 tbsp lavender water
20 drops citrus seed extract
4 drops lavender essential oil**

1. Mix the granules with the kaolin.

2. Add the lavender water to the dry ingredients and mix into a smooth paste.

3. Add the honey, citrus seed extract and lavender pure essential oil to the mixture and ensure that these ingredients are mixed thoroughly.

4. Store the pure lavender scrub in a glass jar.

5. Massage a small quantity over a damp face then rinse off with warm water.

Smooth as silk skin exfoliant

This scrub is filled with rose extracts and is most suitable for dry and delicate skin.

**1 tbsp almond meal
2 tsp pink clay
1 tsp honey
2 tbsp rosewater
1 tsp jojoba oil
1ml (20 drops) citrus seed extract
5 drops rose absolute (optional)**

1. Mix the almond meal with the pink clay.

2. Add the rosewater to these dry ingredients and mix into a smooth paste.

3. Add the honey, jojoba oil, citrus seed extract and rose absolute to the mixture and ensure that these ingredients are mixed thoroughly.

4. Store in a glass jar.

5. Massage a small quantity over a damp face then rinse off with warm water.

plant soothing clay healing herb
caring leaf purifying seed calming
beauty skin exfoliating relaxing nut
cleansing flower moisture mask bud
balm petal gel refreshing massage
salt bath aromatherapy breathing
fruit wellness roots tincture vitamin
infusion balance harmony honey feet
wash plant soothing clay healing
herb caring leaf purifying seed
calming beauty skin exfoliating
relaxing nut cleansing flower
moisture mask bud balm petal gel
refreshing massage salt bath
aromatherapy breathing fruit
wellness roots tincture vitamin
infusion balance bloom create spa

SOAP

- Introduction
- Basic Soap Making
- Hand Milled Soaps
- Glycerin Soaps
- Simple Plant Soaps

Introduction

The Beginnings of Soap Making

The word 'soap' was derived from Mount Sapo which was a location for animal sacrifice. Melted animal fats and wood ashes would be washed down from the mountain and, in the clay along the banks of the River Tiber, a crude soap would form. People found that washing their clothes in this water would result in cleaner clothes. Little has changed in the chemistry of soap making since these early beginnings.

The Chemistry of Soap Making

Soap is made by reacting fats and oils together with lye. The fats and oils may be animal or vegetable in origin and the lye may be a solution of caustic soda (sodium hydroxide) or caustic potash (potassium hydroxide) dissolved in water.

You may have heard that most soaps are made with caustic soda and then, on having heard this, become alarmed, wondering what these soaps have been doing to your skin. Even if a soap is made using caustic soda, a well made soap, once it has 'saponified' and matured properly, will not contain any caustic soda. All of the caustic soda will have reacted with the other ingredients in the soap and undergone a chemical reaction which completely changes its chemical structure and properties. A soapmaker, if asked whether or not their soap contains caustic soda could say truthfully that their soap definitely does not contain caustic soda. Some soapmakers will say they use potash, another substance which you will find is similar to caustic soda. It just doesn't sound quite as dramatic as the words 'caustic soda'.

The natural fats and oils from nuts and seeds used to make soap are esters of the alcohol glycerol and a variety of fatty acids, for example, stearic acid, oleic acid and palmitic acid.

In an example of a soap reaction, coconut oil (mainly stearic acid + glycerol) is acted upon by the caustic soda (sodium hydroxide) to produce a mixture of soap (sodium stearate) and glycerin (glycerol). This reaction is called saponification.

In commercial soaps the glycerol is removed to make the soaps harder and make them last longer. Home-made soaps retain the glycerol which is emollient to the skin giving the soap a milder action on the skin.

Tallow soaps (made with animal fats but may also contain vegetable oils) comprise many of the commercially available products.

Basic Soap Making

Basic Soap Ingredients

Lye

Lye is a constant ingredient in all soaps. It is a strong alkaline solution of caustic soda (sodium hydroxide) or caustic potash (potassium hydroxide) and water. Sodium hydroxide yields hard soaps and potassium hydroxide yields soft or liquid soaps.

In the past, people 'leached' their own lye by running water through wood or plant ashes. The soaps made then were often harsh on the skin and soft in texture.

Sodium hydroxide (caustic soda) which is readily available is now most commonly used in soap making. It is available in most supermarkets and hardware stores among the cleaning supplies.

Water

Water is used to make the lye solution. The caustic soda is dissolved into the water. The water used should be clean, unpolluted rainwater, purified water or bottled spring water. Tap water or 'hard' water contains minerals and impurities which can interfere with the action of the lye and result in a failed batch of soap.

Cautions When Using Lye

- Caustic soda is a strongly alkaline and corrosive substance.

- Wear rubber gloves and cover your benches with newspaper. You may want to consider wearing goggles.

- If you get any caustic soda on your skin, rinse it off within five to ten seconds under running water. Vinegar will help neutralise its alkaline effects.

- Don't breathe in the fumes.

- If swallowed, drink water. Don't induce vomiting. Seek professional help quickly.

- Making soap with lye is not an activity which children should be encouraged to undertake. Keep children and pets away.

- Caustic soda must be added to water. If water is added to caustic soda, the situation could be potentially dangerous as the temperature rises very quickly.

- Never put caustic soda, or soap solutions containing caustic soda, into aluminium, tin, iron or teflon as it corrodes these substances.

- Read the information and cautions on containers of caustic soda.

Fats and oils

As your main fat or oil component in the saponification process, use coconut oil, palm oil, olive oil or vegetable shortening (hydrogenated coconut oil, commonly known as copha, or hydrogenated palm oil) as they saponify readily to give you a hard soap which lathers well.

Other vegetable oils and fats (such as apricot kernel, sweet almond, jojoba, evening primrose, wheatgerm, avocado, shea butter and cocoa butter) which do not allow a solid soap to form, can be added to 'super-fat' the soap and are used for their emollient properties.

Additives

Emollients, exfoliants, colourants and essential oils may constitute up to ten per cent by volume of the total soap mixture. They are usually added just before the soap is ready to pour. If they are added too early, the caustic soda may destroy them or they may interfere with the saponification process.

It is important to remember when making a soap from scratch using only natural ingredients, that the ability to incorporate additives will be limited as they will probably be affected by the reactions going on within the maturing soap.

Emollients

Emollients make a soap very mild and gentle. They include the following moisturising ingredients:

Honey, lecithin, lanolin, glycerin, cocoa butter, shea butter, vegetable oils and infused oils.

The addition of extra oily or fatty substances is called 'super-fatting' a soap. Small quantities of emollients are added once the soap mixture has begun to thicken.

Exfoliants

Exfoliating ingredients are added to soaps to help slough off dead skin cells, keeping the skin smooth. Some of these are:

Ground oats, bran, almond meal, cinnamon, corn meal, poppy seeds, pumice, and sand.

Colourants

Using natural materials is quite difficult as many colours change or fade radically in the presence of lye. Spices and clays make excellent natural soap colouring agents.

- Paprika or annatto will produce light to deep apricot shades.
- Turmeric will produce lemon to yellow colours.
- Saffron or curry powder will produce orange to peach colours.

    The above colours tend to fade quite quickly.

- Cloves, cinnamon and cocoa will produce beige to chocolate colours.
- Green clay, pink clay and yellow clay will add their respective colours to the soap.
- Infused carrot oil will add a golden colour to the soap.

Essential oils

Essential oils may constitute one to four per cent of the total mixture depending on their odour intensity and your skin sensitivity.

Equipment

- Two cooking thermometers (they must register temperatures as low as 20°C and as high as 100°C).
- Measuring scales.
- Large pyrex jug.
- Large pyrex bowl.
- Small pyrex bowl.
- Large stainless steel saucepan.
- Spatula.
- Wooden or stainless steel mixing spoon.
- Rubber gloves.
- Goggles.
- Newspaper.
- Old blankets.
- Moulds. Moulds need to be somewhat flexible and slightly wider at the top than at the bottom so that the soap can be easily removed. Fancy shaped moulds are best used when making hand-milled soaps. The best moulds for soap making with the basic soap recipe are plastic lunch boxes, plastic take-away food containers, ice-cream containers, milk cartons, and microwave containers.

Basic Soap Recipe

Ingredients

500gm hydrogenated coconut oil
(copha) or olive oil
200ml purified water
70gm caustic soda
Emollients up to 20ml
Exfoliants up to 20gm
Colourants up to 20gm
Pure essential oils 7ml up to 20ml

Method

1. Weigh and measure your ingredients.
2. Fill the pyrex jug with the water.
3. Slowly add the caustic soda into the water stirring constantly. Ensure that it has dissolved properly. This solution is now called lye.
4. Leave the lye to cool until the temperature is 35-38°C. It can be made the night before and left to cool as it is easy to heat it up quickly to the correct temperature. If you decide to do this, cover the container so that the solution is not weakened by contact with the air overnight. Otherwise, stand the jug of lye in cold water in the sink to speed up the cooling process.
5. Melt the oils and fats in the pyrex bowl and heat to 35-38°C. Once again, place the bowl in a sink of cold water to adjust the temperature if required.
6. Once both mixtures reach 35-38°C, pour the lye in a slow constant stream into the oils and fats while stirring constantly and smoothly at a medium pace.
7. The correct temperature is important to ensure a proper reaction occurs. If you see too much lye floating on the surface of the fats and oils, while you are pouring the lye solution, stop pouring until the lye has been incorporated properly. Continue pouring and stirring. Do not whip or beat or stir the mixture erratically at this stage.
8. You will begin to see the mixture become opaque and thicken. Using the spoon, drizzle some of the soap mixture across the surface of the soap. When the soap is thick enough to momentarily hold the drizzle on the surface of the mixture, it is ready to pour. (This is known as 'tracing'.)

Note: Making soap with pure olive oil is a very slow process, it may take a day or so for the mixture to thicken. However, after some initial stirring to make sure all the ingredients are well mixed, you only need to stir the soap mixture every so often throughout the day to keep it mixed together. Ensure that the soap mixture is kept in a warm environment in the meantime.

9. The stirring process can take from 15 minutes to around one hour. You can speed up the process by using an electric hand mixer. The mixture will still be warm. It is not unusual for soaps containing only vegetable oils and fats to take up to an hour. If you have been stirring for close to an hour and the soap seems well mixed, and as though it has thickened but will not hold the drizzle on the surface, it should be ready to pour.

10. Add any colours, fragrances, emollients and exfoliants in the following manner.
Remove a small amount of the soap mixture from the bowl and mix your additives into it before incorporating it back into the main soap mixture. Ensure that the additives are mixed in thoroughly. Use an electric hand mixer to ensure an even consistency.

11. Once the additives have been incorporated, pour the finished soap mixture into the mould. Moulds which you would like to reuse should be lined with cling film.

12. Place a lid or cover on top of the mould and wrap in several thick blankets to keep the soap warm. Put in a warm place. You do not want a sudden drop in temperature as this will cause the soap to separate.

13. Leave your soap to solidify. This takes around 24-48 hours. Do not interfere with your soap during this time.

14. After 48 hours, remove the blankets from around the mould and check on your soap. Your soap should be firm but will still be a little soft. If it is too soft, leave it in the mould unwrapped for a day or so to dry and harden. You will then be less likely to damage your soap when trying to remove it.

15. Wearing rubber gloves, gently remove it from the mould. Be careful when doing this as there may be a small amount of lye surrounding the soap.

16. Place the block of soap on a clean surface. The soap will become reasonably firm over the next seven days.

17. Leave your soap to air and finish curing for about four to five weeks. A reaction is still going on though considerably slower. You will notice a slightly powdery layer on your soap. This is sodium carbonate and can be drying to the skin. Slice this off once you have allowed your soap to finish curing.

18. Cut into bars.

19. Voila! You now have ready-to-use bars of soap.

20. Wrap soaps which you will not be using immediately in cellophane, waxed paper or cling film. This reduces the evaporation of any essential oils and keeps the soap fresher.

Soap Making Problems

Problems which occur when making soap are usually due to:

- incorrect measurement of ingredients;
- sudden drops in temperature;
- poor quality ingredients.

Separation

If your mixture is separating in the bowl, heat the mixture again, stirring as it melts. Remove from the heat and continue stirring. Once it thickens, pour it into the mould.

Curdling

If your mixture curdles, it is very difficult to reclaim. Reheating it and adding more fat and/or water may or may not help.

Not thickening

If your mixture isn't thickening, reheat it and then remove it from the heat and keep stirring.

If your mixture won't trace but looks thick, pour it into your mould and cover it more thoroughly with blankets to keep it warm.

Caustic bubbles

Except for a thin coating of soda ash on the surface, your soap should look much the same throughout. Pockets of lye may form in your soap. If this occurs, throw out the batch, as the lye will cause skin irritation.

Layering

If your soap has only slightly layered, slice off the rest of the soap and use the unaffected soap.

Soap Recipes

To get yourself started and to build your confidence in soap making, try one of these gorgeous recipes, using the basic soap recipe on page 71.

Chocolate cake soap

Looks just like chocolate cake and contains many similar ingredients. Absolutely delicious!

500gm hydrogenated coconut oil (copha)
200ml purified water
70gm caustic soda
2 tbsp cocoa powder
1 tbsp cocoa butter

Melt the cocoa butter with the copha in step number 5.

Add the cocoa powder in step number 10.

French angel soap

A gorgeous pink soap with a fragrance which lifts the spirits.

500gm olive oil
200ml purified water
70gm caustic soda
1 tbsp pink or red clay
10ml bergamot essential oil
5ml geranium essential oil

Add the pink or red clay and pure essential oils in step number 10.

Peppermint twist soap

Smells fresh and delicious and looks great.

500gm hydrogenated coconut oil (copha)
200ml purified water
70gm caustic soda
1 tbsp almond oil
1 tbsp green clay
10ml peppermint essential oil

1. Add the essential oil to the soap mixture as per the instructions in step number 10 of the basic soap recipe on page 72.

2. Once the peppermint essential oil has been added back into the soap mixture and stirred in well, remove another small quanitity of the soap mixture and add the green clay and almond oil to it.

3. Pour the rest of the soap mixture into the soap mould.

4. When adding this green clay mixture back into the rest of the soap, swirl it through with a long-handled spoon to create twists throughout the soap.

Hand-Milled Soaps

The hand-milled method is a way of making soaps using a soap base into which other ingredients are incorporated. This method of soap making is the most effective way of incorporating ingredients such as emollients, exfoliants, colourings, and fragrances.

A soap base for making hand-milled soaps can be made from soap which has been made using the basic soap recipe. The soap is grated into small pieces by using a kitchen hand grater. The grated soap will become your soap base.

Other soap bases which you may like to try include blocks of plain soap which have been grated, soap flakes and soap powder, none of which should be fragranced or coloured. If possible choose a soap powder made from plant oils such as palm, coconut or olive oils to make truly luxurious soaps.

Ingredients

250gm soap base (powder or flakes)
250ml-400ml purified water
Exfoliants up to 20gm
Colourants up to 20gm (varies according to the depth of colour you desire)
2.5-3ml (50-60 drops) pure essential oil.

Method

1. Place the soap base and water into a saucepan.

2. Stir the mixture gently until just mixed.

3. Place the saucepan over a gentle heat and heat the mixture gradually.

4. Stir slowly and constantly until the soap has melted. This could take from 30 minutes up to an hour. Be careful not to get carried away and cause the soap to froth and foam or to whip air into it.

5. Once the soap has melted thoroughly, remove from the heat and allow to cool to about 65- 70°C. It should start to thicken.

6. Incorporate your additives. Stir and mix them through well to allow for even dispersion of the ingredients. Stir until the mixture is thick enough not to allow the ingredients to sink to the bottom.

7. Pour or spoon the soap into the moulds making sure there are no air pockets.

8. Smooth over the top of the soap.

9. Allow a skin to form then put in the freezer.

10. Once the soaps have frozen, remove them from the moulds.

11. Place the soaps in a warm, dry spot to allow them to dry and harden without growing mould.

12. This may take a week or two depending on the ingredients used and the size of your soap. (As your soap dries, the loss of moisture will cause your soap to shrink a little.)

Glycerin Soaps

Glycerin soaps are soaps which have a transparent appearance, and not necessarily soaps to which more glycerin has been added. Handmade soaps are glycerin soaps as the natural glycerin has not been removed.

Ingredients

500gm hydrogenated coconut oil (copha)
70gm caustic soda
200ml purified water
118gm granulated white sugar
145gm 80 proof vodka

Method

1. Make the basic soap recipe on page 71.

2. After two days, remove the soap from the mould. It may still be somewhat soft. However, remove it as best you can. It is important to wear gloves while doing this.

3. Grate or cut the soap into tiny pieces.

4. Put the soap into a large pyrex jug and place the jug into a saucepan of water.

5. Place the saucepan on the stove and slowly heat the soap. You want the soap to melt and soften but not to boil.

6. Once the soap has softened and melted, slowly add in the sugar and vodka. Stir slowly and gently. If the soap lathers and bubbles it will not clear properly.

7. Now that the sugar and vodka have been incorporated, allow the mixture to simmer for approximately ten minutes. During this time a reaction will be occurring and the alcohol from the vodka will be evaporating.

8. A small amount of scum will form on the top of the mixture. However, underneath this the soap should be clear. If the soap is still cloudy, remove the scum and leave the soap on the heat a little longer.

9. You will need to test the soap before removing it from the heat. Using a clear glass, spoon about a tablespoon of the soap into the glass and put into the freezer to cool completely. While this is happening, remove the rest of the soap from the heat.

10. If your cooled soap in the glass isn't transparent, reheat the soap mixture and once it looks clear, repeat the test.

11. Remove any scum floating on the top of the soap.

12. Add some drops of carrot oil or beta-carotene to add colour to your soap if you desire. Adding clays or other powders which are opaque will not give you the transparent effect you are trying to achieve. A small amount of dried herbs or petals mixed throughout the soap looks quite effective.

13. Pour the soap mixture into a mould and cure the soap as for the basic soap mixture recipe on page 71.

Simple Plant Soaps

Ingredients

250gm soap base (powder or flakes)
100ml purified water (approximately)
Emollients up to 20ml
Exfoliants up to 20gm
Dried herbs and petals
Colourants up to 20gm (varies according to the depth of colour you desire)
2.5-3ml (50-60 drops) essential oil.

Method

1. Mix the soap base and dry additives together in a bowl.

2. Stir in the water and other additives.

3. Working quickly, knead the ingredients together.

4. Your soap mixture can now be formed into various shapes. You may like to choose one of the following methods:

   • Roll the mixture into balls the size of a plum.

   • Press firmly into moulds ensuring there are no air bubbles.

5. Leave to dry and set properly in a warm, dry, airy spot. The soap balls will dry in about two to three days. The soap pressed into moulds may take approximately a week before it can be removed from the moulds or, alternatively, it can be placed in a freezer until hard then removed from the moulds and put in a place where it can dry.

Daydream soap balls

1 tbsp cocoa butter (grated)
1 tsp dessicated coconut
250gm soap base
100ml water

Chocolate soap balls

1 tbsp cocoa powder
250gm soap base
20ml vanilla essence
100ml water

Good vibrations soap

250gm soap base
20 drops patchouli essential oil
1 tbsp pink clay
100ml water

Lentil bean soap

4 tbsp ground lentils
250gm soap base
5gm powdered benzoin gum
3ml (60 drops) cedarwood essential oil
100ml water

Medieval herbal soap

1 tbsp dried rosemary
1 tbsp fennel seeds
2 tbsp dried sage
250gm soap base
5gm powdered benzoin gum
1ml (20 drops) rosemary essential oil
2ml (40 drops) lemongrass essential oil
100ml water

Wild vanilla soap

250gm soap base
20ml (1 tbsp) vanilla food essence
250gm soap base
100ml water

Calendula petal soap

1 tbsp turmeric
2 tbsp calendula flowers
250gm soap base
3.5ml (70 drops) orange essential oil
100ml water

Cool cucumber soap

1 tbsp green clay
250gm soap base
5gm benzoin powder
3ml (60 drops) petitgrain essential oil
100ml cucumber juice
10 drops citrus seed extract

This soap will need to be used within a couple of weeks.

Sushi soap

1 tbsp powdered seaweed
1 tsp green clay
250gm soap base
40 drops juniper essential oil
100ml water

Persian soap

1 tsp ground cinnamon
1 tbsp rose petals
250gm soap base
10 drops clove essential oil
40 drops mandarin essential oil
20 drops cinnamon essential oil
100ml rosewater

Love soap

1 tbsp pink clay
3 tbsp dried rose petals
250gm soap base
3ml (60 drops) ylang ylang essential oil
100ml water

Your love soap can be rolled in the rose petals to make it look really appealing. Do this while the soap mixture is still very moist.

Or shape into chunky little hearts and press rose petals into them. The petals mixed into the soap will turn brown.

Close shave soap

1 tbsp green clay
250gm soap base
60 drops spike lavender essential oil
20ml sweet almond oil
100ml water

BODY

- Body Washes

- Body Scrubs

- Body Masks

- Body Moisturisers

- Massage Preparations

- Deodorants

- Insect Repellents

- Hair Removal

- Sun

- Talcs

- Hands

- Feet

Body Washes

Body washes are very gentle preparations which are used to cleanse your skin and can be used as an alternative to soaps.

Soapwort body wash

10gm soapwort root
250ml purified water

1. Make a decoction of soapwort root by following the directions on page 24.

2. Strain the soapwort from the decoction.

3. Store in a clean bottle and label. This body wash should be used within three to four days and should be stored in the fridge.

Castile soap body wash

Castile soap is made on pure olive oil and is a very gentle body wash particularly suitable for sensitive skin. Add 20 drops of your favourite essential oil or oils to every 100ml of liquid Castile soap.

Body wash base

A body wash or shower gel base made from plant-derived ingredients which has been made commercially allows you to easily make a customised body wash.

Add 20 drops of your favourite essential oil or oils to every 100ml of the body wash base.

You may like to try an essential oil composition in your body wash. Add one of these essential oil compositions to 100 ml of your body wash base.

Pure Essential Oil Compositions

Alive composition
Fresh and exuberant
8 drops lemongrass
8 drops pine
4 drops Virginian cedarwood

Orange crush composition
Deliciously fruity
6 drops sweet orange
8 drops bergamot
4 drops tangerine

Relaxing composition
Light and relaxing
7 drops lavender
6 drops bergamot
7 drops rosewood

Body Scrubs

Smooth your skin with a body scrub.

Wash your skin first then massage one of these mouthwatering body scrubs all over your body. Rinse, then follow with a beautiful body moisturiser.

Orange marmalade body scrub

This delicious body scrub is suitable for smoothing and moisturising dry skins.

4 tbsp sugar
2 tbsp sweet almond oil
20 drops orange essential oil
1 orange

1. Use your orange to make some orange zest to add to your scrub. To obtain your orange zest grate the skin of your orange.

2. Mix all ingredients together in a bowl and store in a jar.

3. Massage over your skin while bathing.

Lime body smoother

Smooth your skin and be revived with this wonderful body scrub. Suitable for most skin types.

4 tbsp sugar
2 tsp poppy seeds
2 tbsp avocado oil
20 drops lime essential oil

1. Mix all ingredients in a bowl and store in a jar.

2. Massage over your skin while bathing.

Green grapefruit body scrub

This body scrub is superb for smoothing oily and blemished skins.

6 tbsp purified water
2 tbsp green clay
2 tbsp kaolin
2 tbsp semolina
½ tbsp honey
½ tbsp glycerin
20 drops juniper berry essential oil
30 drops grapefruit essential oil
20 drops citrus seed extract

1. Mix all ingredients in a bowl and then store in a jar.

2. Massage over your skin while bathing.

3. This scrub may be applied as a body mask first and left on for ten minutes or so. If the mask has dried, pat on just a small amount of water before massaging it over your body as a scrub.

Banana smoothie body scrub

This is a gentle body scrub for sensitive skins.

1 banana
1 tbsp powdered milk
1 tbsp oatmeal
2 tsp honey

1. Mash your banana then mix together in a bowl with your other ingredients.

2. Massage over your skin while bathing.

3. Use this body scrub within a couple of days of making. Store in the fridge during this time.

Body Masks

Revive and renew your skin with a fresh body mask made especially for you.

Body masks may be used all over the body or used on certain problem areas such as the upper back, shoulders and chest, where there can be pimples, or on areas of skin where there is inflammation or on particularly dry areas of skin. The masks which you make for the face may also be used as body masks.

To use a body mask, wash your skin first and exfoliate with a body scrub if necessary. Apply your body mask to those areas of your skin you desire to treat. Leave the mask on for 15-20 minutes or the time specified in the recipes, then rinse off under the shower. Follow with a body moisturiser.

Paw paw and clay body mask

A cleansing body mask for oily and blemished skins.

3 tbsp kaolin
3 tbsp mashed paw paw
10 drops bergamot essential oil

1. Mash your paw paw then mix it with the kaolin and bergamot essential oil.
2. Apply to your skin for 15-20 minutes.
3. Rinse and remove in the shower with warm water.

Melting mallows body mask

A soothing body mask for sensitive skins.

250ml aloe vera juice
30gm marshmallow root
20gm oatmeal

1. Soak the marshmallow root in aloe vera juice overnight.
2. Strain the marshmallow root from the aloe vera juice the next morning.
3. Stir oatmeal into the remaining aloe vera juice.
4. Apply the paste to your skin and leave on for 15-20 minutes.

If you choose to allow this mixture to dry onto your skin it may be massaged off in circular movements. This will help exfoliate your skin as well.

Sheets of seaweed body mask

A hydrating and healing mask for dry skins.

1. Soak sheets of dried seaweed in water and apply to your skin.
2. Once an area has been covered, wrap with cling film.
3. Leave the seaweed on your skin for at least half an hour before removing.
4. Rinse your skin to remove any remaining seaweed.

Rich cream body mask

A nourishing moisturising mask for dry skins.

Thickened cream applied to dry skin areas will soften and moisturise your skin. The addition of a teaspoon of cold pressed vegetable oil to every tablespoon of thickened cream will moisturise your skin even more.

Purifying body mask

A cleansing body mask for all skin types.

2 handfuls fresh parsley
2 handfuls fresh sage
1 tbsp green clay
1 tbsp natural yoghurt
20 drops lemon essential oil

1. Puree all ingredients into a smooth paste.

2. Apply to your skin for 20 minutes then remove and rinse well in the shower.

See the section on herb poultices (page 28) for packs for various skin problems.

See the section on clays (page 11) for simple clay healing masks for the face and body.

Body Moisturisers

Keep your skin soft and hydrated with one of these skin creams made from plant oils and other beautiful natural ingredients.

Jojoba light body lotion

·If you like a body lotion that feels as if it is instantly absorbed by your skin and doesn't feel greasy try this one. Suitable for all skin types.

Oil phase

20ml jojoba oil
12gm plant-derived emulsifying wax

Water phase

160ml purified water
2ml citrus seed extract

Add at 45°C

40 drops pure essential oil

Choose an essential oil or essential oil composition for your skin type and make the light body lotion by following the directions for making an emulsion on page 36.

Baby bottom balm

This balm will soothe and protect babies' bottoms if they have nappy rash.

15gm cocoa butter
25ml calendula infused oil
60ml apricot kernel oil
10 drops lavender essential oil
5 drops blue chamomile essential oil

To make this balm follow the directions for making an aromatherapy balm on page 30.

Avocado nourishing body lotion

If you like a body lotion which is more nourishing and protective try this one. Suitable for dry skins.

Oil phase

40ml avocado oil
20ml evening primrose oil
2ml (40 drops) vitamin E oil
12gm plant-derived emulsifying wax

Water phase

125ml rosewater
40 drops citrus seed extract
2.5ml (50 drops) pure essential oil

Add at 45°C

40 drops pure essential oil

Choose an essential oil or essential oil composition for your skin type and make the nourishing body lotion by following the directions for making an emulsion on page 36.

Cocoa butter body balm

The balmiest of balms, this cocoa butter body balm is super rich and is suitable for use on very dry skins. It is especially suitable for use during pregnancy to keep your skin soft and supple while it continues to stretch. Use this one to help prevent stretch marks.

15gm cocoa butter
50ml apricot kernel oil
35ml wheatgerm oil
60 drops tangerine essential oil

To make this balm follow the directions for making an aromatherapy balm on page 30.

Massage Preparations

Massage oils and balms lubricate your skin giving you a smooth massage.

Using cold-pressed vegetable oils infused with herbs, or blended with pure essential oils, will fragrance your body and have therapeutic benefits.

Cold pressed vegetable oils enhance the absorption of the essential oils into your skin and give you the lubrication you need for a smooth, soothing massage. As they contain vitamins, they, along with the essential oils, benefit your skin. Vegetable oils such as apricot kernel oil and sweet almond oil make superb massage oil bases as they provide enough lubrication and are eventually absorbed into the surface of the skin.

Herbal infused massage oils

You can use the herbal infused oils you have learned to make on page 25 with cold pressed vegetable oils, herbs and flowers.

Pine, rosemary and **ginger** are excellent choices to infuse for sore, aching muscles.

Infuse **lavender** and **chamomile** flowers to make a relaxing massage oil. They will also relieve irritated, inflamed skin.

Jasmine flowers and **honeysuckle** flowers make a truly luxurious and sensual massage oil. (Jasmine pure essential oil is particularly expensive and if you have an abundance of jasmine flowers take advantage of your good fortune and make this massage oil).

Aromatherapy massage oils

Aromatherapy massage oils are simple to make. Choose your essential oils according to their properties. Enjoy their diverse and enticing aromas as well as their health-giving benefits.

Aromatherapy body massage oil

To make an aromatherapy body massage oil, add up to 2.5 per cent essential oil to a cold-pressed vegetable oil, that is, 50 drops of essential oil to each 100ml of cold-pressed vegetable oil.

Bare body massage oil

This blend of pure cold-pressed vegetable oils may be used on its own or blended with a favourite essential oil or essential oil composition suitable for your skin type. It will nourish and moisturise your skin. A single pure cold pressed vegetable oil may also be used on its own to moisturise your skin (See page 6.).

100ml apricot kernel oil
50ml avocado oil
50ml rosehip oil
100 drops your choice of essential oils

Scar treatment massage oil

35ml wheatgerm oil
15ml carrot infused oil
6 drops frankincense essential oil
9 drops lavender essential oil

Initially, apply the blend to the area around the wound. Once the skin has formed over the top of the wound, massage the blend gently into the skin twice daily.

Eczema and dermatitis massage oil

Eczema is an acute or chronic inflammatory skin condition. It is generally very red and irritated with dry skin, with or without watery vesicles and suppuration.

25ml calendula infused oil
25ml jojoba oil
2 drops lavender essential oil
1 drop blue chamomile essential oil
2 drops yarrow essential oil
4 drops sandalwood essential oil

Apply twice daily, especially after washing.

Beautiful breasts massage oil

A beautiful blend of oils for softening and improving the tone of the skin on the breasts.

8 drops ylang ylang essential oil
10 drops rose absolute
10 drops geranium essential oil
8 drops frankincense essential oil
15ml rosehip oil
85ml apricot kernel oil

Apply after showering.

Massage balms

Massage balms are a very convenient massage product to use. Just dip your fingers into your jar of massage balm and apply the balm to your skin for a massage. Unlike massage oils, balms won't spill.

To make a massage balm, follow the directions for making a balm on page 30 and add your choice of pure essential oils or essential oil compositions.

Cocoa butter massage bars

Solid massage bars are made with cocoa butter and when massaged over the skin they melt (cocoa butter melts at skin temperature). This provides excellent lubrication for a great massage. Pour the following mixture into chocolate moulds to make them look enticing as well.

Cocoa butter massage bars

80gm cocoa butter
20gm coconut oil
50 drops your choice of essential oils

1. Melt the cocoa butter with the coconut oil.
2. Add the drops of pure essential oil or essential oil composition and pour into chocolate moulds.
3. Put into the fridge to harden.
4. Store your massage bars in the fridge in case they melt in the heat.

You may like to choose one of these fragrant essential oil compositions to use in your massage preparations. Add one of these essential oil compositions to 100ml/gm of your massage preparation.

Pure Essential Oil Compositions

Relaxing composition

Induces relaxation

25 drops sweet orange
8 drops sweet marjoram
17 drops lavender

Joyous composition

Positive and uplifting

30 drops bergamot
18 drops geranium
12 drops clary sage

Sensual composition

Rich and seductive

35 drops sweet orange
10 drops patchouli
15 drops ylang ylang

Sore muscle composition

Relieves aching muscles

25 drops spike lavender
20 drops rosemary
15 drops ginger

Dream composition

For sweet dreams

30 drops distilled lime
20 drops geranium
10 drops frankincense

Detoxifying composition

Enhances lymphatic drainage

25 drops lemon
15 drops juniper
5 drops carrot seed
10 drops peppermint

Floral composition

Sweet and fresh

10 drops lavender
4 drops ylang ylang
6 drops geranium

Precious patchouli composition

Warm and earthy

6 drops patchouli
8 drops Atlas cedarwood
12 drops bergamot

Deodorants

Pure essential oil used in combination with other ingredients, such as apple cider vinegar, benzoin tincture and myrrh tincture, may be used to keep your underarms smelling pleasant.

Unlike antiperspirants, deodorants do not interfere with your body's natural secretion of perspiration. What they do is mask any offensive body odour. Some deodorants may actually kill the bacteria which cause the odour as they feed off your secretions.

Choose from the following essential oils to make a deodorant you would like to wear:

> bergamot, cedarwood, clary sage, cypress, eucalyptus, frankincense, geranium, juniper, lavender, patchouli, pine, rosewood, sandalwood, tea tree, ylang ylang.

Deodorant block

85gm cocoa butter
15gm beeswax
60 drops your choice of essential oils
15gm bicarbonate soda
1 tbsp dried herbs

1. Melt the beeswax and cocoa butter together.

2. Add the bicarbonate of soda and dried herbs and mix thoroughly with an electric hand mixer.

3. Once the mixture has cooled a little add the essential oils.

4. Pour the mixture into a mould such as a plastic cup. The herbs will float to the top and make it look fantastic.

5. Once your deodorant block has set, remove it from the container.

6. Use the side which does not have the herbs on it as they may feel a little uncomfortable on your armpit.

7. You may need to store it in the fridge in hot weather.

Deodorant spray

60 drops your choice of essential oils
80ml purified water
30ml apple cider vinegar
10ml benzoin tincture
5ml myrrh tincture

1. Blend the pure essential oils with the apple cider vinegar, benzoin tincture, and myrrh tincture.

2. Add this mixture to the water in a spray bottle and shake well. It is now ready for use at anytime.

Aromatic vinegar deodorant

60 drops your choice of essential oils
30ml apple cider vinegar
95ml purified water

1. Blend the essential oils with the apple cider vinegar.

2. Add this mixture to the water in a spray bottle and shake well. This instant deodorant is now ready for use whenever you need it.

Herbal vinegar deodorant

30ml herbal vinegar
95ml purified water

1. See page 26 for information on making a fragrant herb vinegar.

2. Shake the herb vinegar together with the water in a spray bottle. It is now ready for use at any time.

Deodorant powder

Use this deodorant powder to absorb excess perspiration and to add the fragrance of pure essential oils to your body.

50gm orris root powder
50gm cornstarch
60 drops your choice of essential oils

1. Mix the orris root powder and cornstarch together.

2. Slowly add the pure essential oils drop by drop while stirring.

3. Shake the mixture through a seive ensuring any lumps are broken down as you go.

4. Store the powder in an old talcum powder container or in a stainless steel parmesan cheese shaker or icing sugar container both of which are available at kitchen shops.

You may like to choose one of these fragrant essential oil compositions to use in your deodorant. Add one of these essential oil compositions to 100ml/gm of your deodorant preparation.

Pure Essential Oil Compositions

Fresh composition	Deep forest composition	Soft composition
Fresh and clean		*Soft and gentle*
30 drops bergamot	*Fresh and woody*	25 drops lavender
10 drops cypress	18 drops pine	20 drops rosewood
20 drops geranium	24 drops distilled lime	15 drops ylang ylang
	8 drops Virginian cedarwood	

Insect Repellents

Many essential oils have been traditionally used very effectively to repel mosquitos and other nasty insects that bite.

The following essential oils can be used in repellents:

> cajeput, Virginian cedarwood, citronella, eucalyptus, geranium, lavender, lemongrass, peppermint, rosemary, spike lavender, tea tree.

The essential oils are used by blending them with any of the following bases.

Insect repellent body oil

Add 60 drops of your choice of the above essential oils to 100ml of sweet almond oil or apricot kernel oil.

Insect repellent cream

Add 60 drops of your choice of the above essential oils to 100gm of cream base (see page 37 for instructions).

Insect repellent balm

Add 60 drops of to 100gm of balm base (see page 30 for instructions).

Insect repellent spray

70ml perfume alcohol base
30ml water
or
100ml vodka
or
70ml vinegar
30ml water

1. Add 60 drops of your choice of the above essential oils to the perfume alcohol base or vinegar.

2. Then add the water to this mixture and shake well. Otherwise add the essential oil directly to the vodka.

3. Pour into a spray bottle.

Mosquito bite relief oil

Apply pure lavender or tea tree essential oil, with a cotton wool ball, directly to a mosquito bite. Hold the cotton wool ball against the mosquito bite until the itch subsides.

You may like to choose one of the following essential oil compositions to use in your insect repellent. Add one of these essential oil compositions to 100ml/gm of your insect repellent preparation.

Pure Essential Oil Compositions

Great outdoors composition
20 drops lemongrass
25 drops spike lavender
15 drops pine

Summer nights composition
20 drops geranium
20 drops eucalyptus
20 drops citronella

Hair Removal

If you like to have a smooth, hairless skin 'Sugaring' is a method which is easy to apply, and very effective in removing hair.

Sugaring

Sugar has been used to remove body hair in the Middle East for many years. This is a very simple recipe which can be made up whenever it is needed or stored in a heatproof container and melted down when required.

As the mixture is water soluble any drips or spills are easily cleaned up. However, if your skin is moist, the sugaring mixture will not adhere as well. Therefore it is important to dust your skin with talc before sugaring.

Sugar depilator

500gm granulated sugar
Juice of one lemon
10ml glycerin
Calico strips
Spatula or smooth butter knife

1. Add the lemon juice to the sugar.

2. Mix and heat in a saucepan for ten minutes or until the sugar is caramelised to a golden brown.

3. Remove from the heat then add the glycerin.

4. Lightly dust your legs with talc.

5. Apply the sugaring, with a spatula, in strips down your leg in the direction of hair growth. Make the application as thin as possible.

6. Smooth calico strips over the strips of sugaring in the direction of hair growth.

7. To remove the hairs and sugaring from the legs, rip the calico strip, gripping the bottom edge, against the direction of hair growth. Do not pull straight up but parallel to the leg.

8. Re-use the calico strip until the sugaring has built up on it too thickly to be effective.

9. Rinse off any sticky bits left on your hands or legs with water.

10. Apply a soothing oil, lotion or gel.

After waxing skin soother

To calm redness after waxing or sugaring apply this calming massage oil blend to the skin. The essential oils chosen are not only anti-inflammatory but are also antiseptic.

20 drops lavender essential oil
8 drops blue chamomile essential oil
12 drops rosewood essential oil
25ml calendula infused oil
75ml apricot kernel oil

The essential oils may also be added to the base cream recipe on page 37.

Sun

A deep tan used to be a sign of wealth and good health because only the rich could afford to lie around in the sun all day. Fortunately, we now realise that a tan indicates little more than damaged skin, unless you are lucky enough to be born with naturally brown or dark skin.

Faking the tan

Strong black tea is the answer to a tan without baking in the sun. Make a strong cup of black tea, strain it (don't drink it) and sponge it over those areas which you desire to be tanned. You can build up depth of colour by applying it in layers, allowing it to dry in between each application.

Sunburn treatments

When your skin has been scorched by the sun, cooling and anti-inflammatory preparations are called for.

Aloe vera gel

Slice it fresh from the plant or squeeze it from a bottle if you don't have one of these fabulous succulents in your garden. If purchasing aloe vera gel, look for one which is as pure as possible. Apply the aloe vera gel to your sunburn regularly. As soon as your sunburn heats up again, apply some more. Keep your aloe vera gel in the fridge.

Cucumber

Take your cucumber straight from the refrigerator and cut it into thick strips lengthways and rub these over your sunburn. Use as often as necessary to soothe and cool.

Yoghurt

Smooth cool natural yoghurt over your skin to relieve sunburn. Once the yoghurt dries on your skin, rinse with cool water and smooth on more yoghurt.

Apple cider vinegar

Add one cup of apple cider vinegar to two cups of cold water and spray or splash over your skin as often as necessary to take the sting out of sunburn.

Tea

Pour a cup of boiling water over four teaspoons or teabags of black tea. Strain the tea and add several ice cubes. Blot the cooled liquid all over your sunburn with cotton wool pads or an old cloth. This will soothe the irritation.

Oatmeal

Tie a handful of oatmeal in a square of cloth and use it in a cool bath with you. Squeeze the wet oatmeal bag into the water and over your skin. This is great for soothing any irritated skin.

Essential oils

Add 20 drops of lavender or chamomile pure essential oil to 100ml of your body lotion and slather it over your body or add 20 drops to 100ml of a dispersing bath oil base and pour one to two tablespoons into a cool bath to calm and soothe your sunburn.

Chamomile tea

Make a bowl of chamomile tea and add ice cubes or put in the fridge to cool. Use a cloth to dip into the cool chamomile tea and place it over your sunburn. Reapply several times to reduce the soreness and redness of your sunburn.

Burn healing and soothing gel

50ml aloe vera gel
5 drops lavender essential oil

Mix the lavender oil into an aloe vera gel base and apply to the burned area. Reapply the gel each time the area heats up. Keep the gel in the fridge for a cooling effect.

Talcs

Applying talcs is another wonderful way to fragrance your body as well as to absorb excess moisture.

Pure talc, cornstarch, and kaolin make excellent fine-textured powders. Pure talc has the finest texture followed by cornstarch and then kaolin. You may choose to use one of these ingredients or a mixture of these ingredients.

Orris root powder is often added to powders for its absorbent properties. Used by itself, it can be a little too coarse. You may like to try one of these basic talc recipes and add your own choice of essential oil or use one of the beautiful essential oil compositions.

To make your talcum powders, follow these directions.

1. Slowly add your choice of essential oils drop by drop to the talc base, stirring them in as you go.

2. Shake the mixture through a seive, breaking down any lumps which may have occurred.

3. Store your talcum powder in an old talc container or in a stainless steel parmesan cheese shaker or icing sugar shaker, both of which are available at kitchen shops.

Cornstarch body talc

100gm talc powder
50gm cornstarch
40 drops your choice of essential oils

Baby powder

100gm cornflour
10gm dried calendula flowers
(finely ground)
10gm dried chamomile flowers
(finely ground)
20gm zinc oxide powder
10 drops lavender essential oil

Orris root body talc

120gm kaolin
30gm orris root powder
40 drops your choice of essential oils

Choose one of these essential oil compositions to add to one of the talc bases above.

Pure Essential Oil Compositions

Exotica composition	Heaven composition	Pleasure composition
9 drops cinnamon	12 drops lavender	15 drops ylang ylang
8 drops petitgrain	10 drops may chang	5 drops vetiver
8 drops palmarosa	10 drops spearmint	20 drops bergamot
15 drops orange	8 drops geranium	

Hands

Soft, clean, warm, caring ... They are exposed to everything including the scorching sun, washing up detergents and soft baby's skin.

Slather your hands with a softening, smoothing, moisturising hand cream and keep them looking and feeling great!

Virgin hand cream

Soften and smooth your hands with this moisturising hand cream.

Oil phase

80ml virgin olive oil
5gm plant-derived emulsifying wax

Water phase

80ml rosewater
¼ tsp honey
1ml (20 drops) citrus seed extract

Add at 45°C

1.5ml (30 drops) geranium essential oil

Make your virgin moisturising hand cream by following the instructions on making an emulsion on page 36.

Glove treatment for gorgeous hands

This is a wonderful treatment for treating dry, damaged and wrinkled hands. As well as softening the skin, this treatment acts as a barrier preventing water loss from the skin. As a result any water in the skin is forced back into the surface layers of skin cells hydrating and softening them.

10ml (2 tsp) lecithin
30gm shea butter
10ml wheatgerm oil

1. Melt all the ingredients together in a bain-marie stirring them together well.

2. Pour the mixture into a jar. Allow the mixture to cool and set.

3. Massage this rich treatment into your skin.

4. Put on a pair of cotton gloves, then a pair of plastic gloves over these and leave on overnight. In the morning your hands will feel gorgeous.

Myrrh healing hand balm

This is a rich emollient balm for dry, cracked and damaged hands. It is formulated to leave the hands feeling soft and smooth.

Oil phase

30ml avocado oil
15ml carrot infused oil
15gm shea butter
8gm plant-derived emulsifying wax

Water phase

30ml purified water
10 drops citrus seed extract

Add at 45°C

15 drops lavender essential oil
15 drops myrrh essential oil

Make the myrrh healing hand balm by following the instructions for making an emulsion on page 36.

Superb soothing hand cream

This hand cream contains ingredients to soothe red, irritated and itchy hands and to moisturise dry skin.

Oil phase

40ml avocado oil
10ml calendula infused oil
15gm cocoa butter
5gm beeswax
5gm plant-derived emulsifying wax

Water phase

40ml aloe vera juice
5ml vegetable glycerin
1ml (20 drops) citrus seed extract

Add at 45°C

15 drops lavender essential oil
5 drops blue chamomile essential oil

Make the superb soothing hand cream by following the instructions for making an emulsion on page 36.

Citrus smoothing hand scrub

This citrus scrub is superb for softening and smoothing dry hands. It also helps remove stains and ingrained dirt.

50ml avocado oil
2 tbsp salt
20 drops lemon essential oil

Mix all ingredients together in a bowl and store in a jar. Use a teaspoonful or so and massage over dampened hands. Once you have massaged your hands well, rinse them off. You will notice that your hands will feel soft and smooth and a thin layer of oil will remain on your skin.

Rosewood cuticle cream

Cuticle creams are used to soften the cuticles preventing them from becoming dry and cracked. It also makes them easy to push back.

Oil phase

4gm shea butter
50ml apricot kernel oil
12gm beeswax
4gm plant-derived emulisfying wax

Water phase

30ml purified water
1ml (20 drops) citrus seed extract

Add at 45°C

15 drops rosewood essential oil

Make the rosewood cuticle cream by following the instructions for making an emulsion on page 36.

Grapefruit nail enhancing oil

50ml sweet almond oil
15 drops grapefruit essential oil

Massage this blend into the skin at the base of your nail, where your nail begins to grow, and over the nail itself. The massage will stimulate circulation to the nail encouraging better growth and the oil will reduce nail brittleness.

Feet

Narrow, fat, sore, cracked ... Feet, just take a look, are as individual as we are. They take the load for all of us. Treat them well and you will notice how much better the rest of you feels too. Rejuvenate, heal and moisturise your feet with pure essential oils and plant based preparations.

Recovery foot and leg massage oil

Use this wonderful massage oil to soothe your aching feet and legs.

**13 drops spike lavender essential oil
8 drops eucalyptus essential oil
7 drops peppermint essential oil
22 drops lemon essential oil
100ml sweet almond oil**

Blend your essential oils into the sweet almond oil and store in an amber glass bottle. Massage a small quantity into your legs and feet or, even better, have somebody else do it for you.

Chill-out foot and leg gel

Soothe and revive your tired, aching legs with this cool gel. Smooth it over your legs whenever you feel like it.

**2gm xanthan gum
100ml purified water
10 drops peppermint essential oil
10 drops lavender essential oil**

1. To make your chill-out foot and leg gel, follow the instructions for making a plant gel on page 31.

2. Add your essential oils and stir in thoroughly.

3. Store in a clean container.

Soothing moisturising foot cream

Keep the skin on your feet smooth with this easily absorbed moisturising cream. The essential oils are very soothing and cooling.

Oil phase

**40ml sweet almond oil
5gm plant-derived emulsifying wax**

Water phase

**100ml purified water
5ml vegetable glycerin
1.25ml (25 drops) citrus seed extract**

Add at 45°C

**20 drops lavender essential oil
10 drops spearmint essential oil**

Make your moisturising foot cream by following the directions for making an emulsion on page 36. Massage it into your feet each morning and night to keep your feet soft and moisturised.

Healing foot balm

We all suffer from dry, cracked feet at some time, especially when we neglect to take good care of them. Use this healing foot balm to soften, moisturise and heal those cracks.

Oil phase

**10gm beeswax
30ml avocado oil
10ml wheatgerm oil
15gm shea butter
5gm plant-derived emulsifying wax**

Water phase

**30ml water
5ml vegetable glycerin
1ml (20 drops) citrus seed extract**

Add at 45°C

**25 drops lavender essential oil
25 drops myrrh essential oil**

Make your healing foot balm by following the instructions for making an emulsion on page 36.

Foot Scrubs

Smooth your feet with a granular exfoliant made from coarsely ground nuts, grains or dried pulses. Coarsely ground salt or sugar will also remove dry skin from your feet.

Mix your granules into a paste using water or milk or yoghurt with some honey and cold pressed vegetable oil. The water, milk and yoghurt provide moisture to make the paste, the honey binds the ingredients while the cold pressed vegetable oil softens the skin.

Volcanic rock foot scrub

A smoothing, fresh fragranced foot scrub.

**2 tbsp crushed pumice stone
1 tbsp kaolin
1 tbsp honey
1 tbsp sweet almond oil
1.5 tbsp purified water
25 drops lemon essential oil
10 drops pine essential oil
10 drops citrus seed extract**

1. Mix the crushed pumice stone and kaolin together so that the pumice stone is mixed evenly throughout the kaolin.
2. Add the water, then sweet almond oil and honey and mix into a smooth paste.
3. Finally add the essential oils and citrus seed extract.

4. Store in a clean jar.

Soak your feet first, so that your skin is soft, then massage the foot scrub all over them to remove any rough bits.

Foot Baths

Bath oils, salts or vinegars are blended with pure essential oils to make therapeutic soaks for your feet.

Soothing foot baths

A wonderful soak for tired, aching, swollen feet and ankles.

Soothing foot bath oil

**25 drops lavender essential oil
10 drops juniper essential oil
10 drops geranium essential oil
15 drops spearmint essential oil
100ml dispersing bath oil**

1. Add the pure essential oils to 100 ml of dispersing bath oil and shake.
2. Use two teaspoons of the soothing foot bath oil in a basin of warm water.

Soothing foot bath salts

**25 drops lavender essential oil
10 drops juniper essential oil
10 drops geranium essential oil
15 drops spearmint essential oil
200gm epsom salts**

1. Add the essential oils to the epsom salts, stirring them well throughout the salts.
2. Put the mixture into a closed container to allow the essential oils to absorb for approximately a week before using them.
3. Add one tablespoon of the soothing foot salts to a basin of warm water.

Deodorising foot baths

You can control bad foot odour by choosing to use herbs and essential oils which are both antiseptic and fabulously fragrant. Soak your feet in these foot baths and enjoy the difference.

Funky foot bath

An excellent foot bath for deodorising your feet.

100ml dispersing bath oil
5 drops cypress essential oil
10 drops lemongrass essential oil
5 drops peppermint essential oil
10 drops spike lavender essential oil

1. Mix all of the ingredients together and store in an amber glass bottle.

2. Add two teaspoons of the funky foot bath oil to a basin of water and soak your feet for ten to 15 minutes before towelling them dry.

Sage vinegar foot soak

A great foot soak to deodorise anybody's smelly feet.

2 tbsp sage herb
2 tbsp rosemary herb
2 tbsp thyme herb
2 tbsp peppermint herb
1 tbsp lemon peel
1½ cups apple cider vinegar

1. Make the sage vinegar foot soak by following the directions for making a herbal vinegar on page 26.

2. Add two tablespoons to a basin of water and soak your feet for ten to 15 minutes before towelling them dry.

Warming foot baths

Soak your feet in these preparations to stimulate the circulation in your feet and to warm your feet.

Mustard soak

This is a traditional remedy for warming cold feet.

Add one teaspoon of mustard powder to a basin of hot water and place your feet in there to soak.

Ginger and rosemary foot soak

30 drops ginger essential oil
30 drops rosemary essential oil
100ml dispersing bath oil

1. Blend the essential oils into the dispersing bath oil.

2. Add two teaspoons of the foot soak to a basin of hot water and place your feet in there to soak.

Foot Powders

Foot powders are used to absorb excess moisture and perspiration from your feet, to deodorise your feet and may be used as part of a treatment for athlete's foot.

Blend the following essential oil compositions or your own specific choice of essential oils into the foot powder base.

Foot powder base

75gm talc or kaolin
25gm orris root powder

This is an excellent absorbent mixture for the feet. (Any of these ingredients may also be used by themselves).

1. Mix together the talc or kaolin and orris root powder in a large mixing bowl.
2. Add the essential oils drop by drop stirring them in as you go.
3. Once you have incorporated all of the essential oils, stir the mixture thoroughly.
4. Sift the powder through a sieve several times ensuring any moist clumps are broken down each time.
5. Store your powder in an airtight container and use as desired.

Special Foot Treatments

Blister treatment

Dab blisters regularly with a couple of drops of lavender pure essential oil. This will soothe them, help dry them up and heal them quickly.

Anti-fungal foot treatment

This lotion is effective in treating tinea due to its anti-fungal properties and its ability to dry up any moisture which encourages fungal growth.

50ml tincture of myrrh
30 drops tea tree essential oil

Blend the ingredients together in an amber glass bottle. Apply the lotion twice a day, especially after your feet have been in water.

Choose one of these pure essential oil compositions to add to the foot powder base on the previous page.

Pure Essential Oil Compositions

Foot deodorant composition
20 drops lemon essential oil
14 drops pine essential oil
8 drops geranium essential oil
8 drops patchouli

Athlete's foot composition
15 drops tea tree essential oil
15 drops thyme essential oil
20 drops spike lavender essential oil

BATHS

- **Bath Preparations**

Bath Preparations

Slip off your robe and ease yourself into the tub, lie back, close your eyes and take a deep breath. Let your body become weightless, your arms float to the surface, and your fingers relax and open. This is the perfect time to let your imagination run free. Surrender your fantasies to these most creative, beautiful and luxurious bath recipes.

The ritual of bathing must be one of the most therapeutic experiences. A wonderful treatment physically, mentally and spiritually.

Aromatherapy Baths

Pure essential oils used in bath preparations are incredibly therapeutic. They can relieve aching muscles, revive flagging spirits and can be used to create wonderfully sensual baths for lovers or a sanctuary for those who need time out.

Essential oils can be used in the following bath preparations - bath oils, bath bombs, bubble baths, bath salts, and soda baths.

It is important to dilute your essential oils properly before adding them to your bath as skin irritation may result from sitting directly on the oils which are floating on the surface of the water.

Choose from the following essential oils to add to your bath.

- **Calming and relaxing**
  Cedarwood, chamomile, frankincense, geranium, lavender, marjoram,

patchouli, rosewood, sandalwood, vetiver and ylang ylang.

- **Invigorating and reviving**
  Eucalyptus, grapefruit, lemon, lemongrass, peppermint, pine and rosemary.
- **Uplifting**
- Bergamot, geranium, lemon balm, lime, mandarin, may chang, neroli, orange, palmarosa, petitgrain, tangerine.
- **Skin soothing**
  Chamomile, everlasting, lavender and yarrow.
- **Aching bodies**
  Cajeput, ginger, spike lavender, marjoram, black pepper, pine and rosemary.

Herbal Baths

Herbs can be used in many bath preparations including bath oils, bath vinegars, infusions, decoctions, and bath bags. They can be added to bath salts purely for decoration.

Choose from the following herbs to make your herbal bath preparations.

- **Calming and relaxing**
  Chamomile, geranium leaves, hops, lavender, lemon balm, lime flowers, valerian.
- **Invigorating and reviving**
  Bay leaves, eucalyptus, lemongrass, peppermint, pine, thyme, orange, lemon and grapefruit peels.
- **Aching bodies**
  Eucalyptus, ginger root, lavender, mustard, and rosemary.

Bubble Baths

Fun, laughter and luxury are what bubble baths are all about. Loads of bubbles and exotic aromas surround you as you enjoy the experience. In order to create your own exquisite bubble bath it is important to procure a good plant-derived bubble bath base. (Making your bubble bath from basic ingredients is an uneconomical alternative as the ingredients are available only in large, bulk quantities. This makes the purchasing of these ingredients prohibitive to the individual bubble bath maker).

Add your choice of pure essential oils to a bubble bath base. A one per cent dilution is recommended as the addition of more essential oil than this will reduce your bubble bath's foaming action and consequently the amount of bubbles.

Choose your favourite essential oil to add to the bubble bath base or add one of the pure essential oil compositions on this page to 100ml of bubble bath base.

Children's bubble baths

Children love their baths filled with bubbles. Citrus essential oils such as lime, orange, mandarin and tangerine make delicious smelling bubble baths for children. Lavender and chamomile can be added to calm and soothe kids on the go.

You may like to choose one of these pure essential oil compositions to enjoy in your bubble baths.

Pure Essential Oil Compositions

Relaxing bubble bath
Relax both body and mind
11 drops orange
6 drops lavender
3 drops marjoram

Anti-stress bubble bath
To calm those nerves and lift your spirits
4 drops geranium
2 drops clary sage
8 drops orange

Sensual bubble bath
A lovers' bath
8 drops bergamot
5 drops ylang ylang
10 drops sandalwood

A secret place bubble bath
Revitalising and strengthening
7 drops bergamot
4 drops frankincense
9 drops sandalwood

Zest bubble bath
Totally refreshing
10 drops lemon
6 drops pine
4 drops rosemary

Happy lime bubble bath
Lots of fun
10 drops lime, distilled
10 drops orange

The amazing mandarin bubble bath
Totally delicious
16 drops mandarin or tangerine
4 drops ylang ylang

Big day out bubble bath
Very relaxing
15 drops lavender
5 drops Roman chamomile

Bath Oils

Bath oils are a wonderful way to moisturise your skin as well as being one of the best ways to use essential oils for their pure natural fragrances and their therapeutic properties.

Dispersing bath oils

The most effective way of using essential oils in the bath is by using a dispersing bath oil. This method ensures that the essential oils are dispersed properly throughout the bath water. If essential oils are dropped directly into bath water without any kind of dispersant, they will float in their concentrated form on top of the bath water. When you go to sit in the bath water your bare thighs and bottom come into direct contact with the essential oils and burning and irritation may result.

A dispersing bath oil is made from a modified vegetable oil and is used for the purpose of dispersing essential oils throughout the bath water. It also leaves the skin feeling soft and moisturised. It does not leave a slippery, oily residue on the bath.

To make your own dispersing bath oils try the following recipes.

Smooth honey dispersing bath oil

75ml almond oil
5ml honey
**20ml alcohol (such as a natural
perfume alcohol base or vodka)**
60 drops your choice of essential oils

Mix the ingredients and use 20ml (1 tbsp) in your bath water.

Liquid Castile dispersing bath oil

Castile liquid soap is an excellent base for dispersing your essential oils throughout the bath water. Add 20-30 drops of essential oil to 100ml of Castile soap. Add 20ml (1 tbsp) of this mixture to the bath water.

Almond Castile dispersing bath oil

50ml almond oil
50ml Castile liquid soap
60 drops your choice of essential oils

Mix the ingredients and use 20ml in your bath water.

Floating bath oils

Floating bath oils float on the surface of the bath water. They leave an emollient film on your skin as you step out of the bath. They leave a slippery residue on your bath so it is important to wipe over your bath after using these oils.

Cold-pressed vegetable oils are recommended for making floating bath oils. They can be used as they are or, alternatively, an aromatherapy bath oil can be made with them. Herbal infused oils can also be used for a fragrant and therapeutic bath (see page 25).

An aromatherapy bath oil can be made by adding 20-60 drops of essential oil to 100ml of cold-pressed vegetable oil. Add 10-20ml to the bath water and swirl it throughout the water.

Bath Vinegars

The addition of apple cider vinegar to the bath water helps restore your skin's acid mantle and reduces skin irritation. It can be added to the water as it is or you can make a fragrant herb vinegar with herbs of your choice (see page 26). Add a half to one cup of the vinegar to the bath water.

Fresh herbs bath vinegar

Gorgeously fragrant, this bath vinegar is made with fresh herbs.

3 tbsp fresh lavender flowers
3 tbsp fresh geranium leaves
2 tbsp fresh rosemary leaves
250ml (1 cup) apple cider vinegar

Fresh lavender, geranium and rosemary picked from your garden should be soaked in vinegar for a couple of weeks before using.

Soda Baths

Bicarbonate of soda or sodium bicarbonate added to the bath reduces skin irritations. One tablespoon of bicarbonate of soda can be added directly to the bath for this purpose.

Essential oils can be added by mixing ten drops with each 100gm of bicarbonate of soda. Stir the oils in well. Store in an airtight container, shaking daily for a week before using. This allows for better absorption of the essential oils into the bicarbonate of soda.

Sprinkle dried herbs and flowers throughout the mixture for a colourful effect.

Bare skins soda bath

A great bath for irritated or itchy skins.

40gm (2 tbsp) bicarbonate of soda
2 drops blue chamomile essential oil
4 drops lavender essential oil
5gm (1 tsp) crumbled cocoa butter

Mix the cocoa butter throughout the bicarbonate of soda then add the essential oils to the mixture following the directions given above.

Bath Bombs

Bicarbonate of soda when mixed with citric acid creates a wonderful fizzy bath when thrown into the water.

Basic bath bomb

80gm (4 tbsp) bicarbonate soda
20gm (1 tbsp) citric acid
1ml (20 drops) essential oil
1 tsp Argiletz clay of your choice
dried flower petals, herbs or spices (optional)

1. Mix all dry ingredients together in a bowl.

2. Sprinkle the essential oils throughout the mixture then mix through thoroughly.

3. Press the mixture into a mould as firmly as possible. The following items may be used as moulds: candle moulds, chocolate moulds (to make little ones), muffin tins, small plastic food containers, jelly moulds.

    If using petals and such to decorate your bath bombs, sprinkle a few into the mould first so that they will be visible on the surface of the bath bombs.

4. Leave the mixture in the mould for a day to set.

5. Gently remove the bath bomb from the mould.

6. Leave for another day to allow the bath bomb to harden.

7. Your bath bomb is now ready for you to enjoy.

Beautiful fizzy stuff

Throw this one into the bath, enjoy the fizz and the wonderful aroma.

80gm (4 tbsp) bicarbonate of soda
20gm (1 tbsp) citric acid
1 tbsp dried rose and calendula petals
20 drops geranium essential oil

Make your beautiful fizzy stuff by following the basic bath bomb recipe.

Exploding oranges

80gm (4 tbsp) bicarbonate of soda
20gm (1 tbsp) citric acid
½ tsp pink or red clay
½ tsp yellow clay
20 drops orange essential oil

Make your exploding oranges by following the basic bath bomb recipe.

Cocoa butter bombs

Cocoa butter bombs will help moisturise your skin.

80gm (4 tbsp) bicarbonate of soda
20gm (1 tbsp) citric acid
3 tsp crumbled cocoa butter
20 drops lavender essential oil

Make your cocoa butter bombs by following the basic bath bomb recipe.

Bran and Oat Baths

Bran and/or oat baths are wonderfully soothing to the skin. They are superb for itchy and irritated skin. Your skin will feel calm and smooth after one of these treats.

Tie a handful of bran and/or oats in a square of cheesecloth or muslin, dip it into your bath and squeeze to release a milky fluid. Massage the bag over your skin to cleanse it.

You can mix the bran and/or oats with other herbs of your choice and with powdered milk for a fragrant milky bath. Use these preparations only once before discarding them.

Ahhhh skin soother oat bath

A bath treat to soothe red, irritated skin.

In your square of cheesecloth or muslin, tie the following skin soothing dried herbs and ingredients.

3 tbsp rolled oats
1 tbsp chamomile flowers
1 tbsp calendula flowers
1 tbsp lavender flowers

Transylvanian delight

A dreamy, fragrant bath treat which also moisturises your skin.

In your square of cheesecloth or muslin, tie the following fragrant dried herbs and moisturising ingredients.

3 tbsp rolled oats
2 tbsp crumbled cocoa butter
1 tbsp rose petals
1 tbsp lavender flowers
1 tbsp peppermint leaves

Bath Salts

Epsom salts are great to relax in as they help relieve tired, sore muscles.

Aromatherapy bath salts can be made by adding up to 1ml (20 drops) of pure essential oil to every 100gm of Epsom salts.

Natural colour and texture can be achieved by sprinkling dried herbs and petals or coloured clays throughout the salts. A half a teaspoon of clay is sufficient to colour 200gm of bath salts. Add the clay to the bath salts before mixing in the essential oils. Once you have mixed all ingredients thoroughly, put in an airtight container and leave for a week. This allows the bath salts to absorb the essential oils.

Rose petal bath salts

A real luxury — very pink and pretty.
200gm Epsom salts
1 tbsp dried rose petals
½ tsp pink clay
20 drops geranium essential oil

Leaves and things bath salts

A revitalising bath.
200gm Epsom salts
5 drops spearmint essential oil
7 drops geranium essential oil
8 drops lavender essential oil
1 tsp dried peppermint leaves
1 tsp dried lavender flowers

Hot zone bath salts

A warming bath for those feeling the cold or those who have caught a cold.
200gm Epsom salts
10 drops ginger essential oil
10 drops black pepper essential oil

Aching body bath salts

For when you have been working or playing hard or have sore muscles and joints.
200gm Epsom salts
10 drops rosemary essential oil
10 drops spike lavender essential oil
10 drops ginger essential oil

Detox bath salts

This combination of essential oils and Epsom salts can be used as part of a detoxification programme.

200gm Epsom salts
10 drops lemon essential oil
6 drops juniper essential oil
4 drops cypress essential oil

(Naturopaths often recommend the addition of up to 500gm of plain epsom salts to a bath for a strong detoxifying effect. This should only be carried out after consultation and recommendation by a qualified naturopath.

Honey Baths

Honey soothes and softens the skin. Dissolve one tablespoon of honey in some hot water. Pour this into your bath water and swirl it throughout the water.

Milk Baths

Milk soothes and softens the skin. Fresh milk can be added directly to the bath.

Full cream milk can also be used to help disperse essential oils throughout the bath water. However, only a few drops should be added to the milk using this method. Add one to two drops of essential oil to one tablespoon of full cream milk.

Powdered milk can be used in bath bags along with herbs, oats or bran for a fragrant, soothing, milky bath.

Coconut milk added to your bath water is very soothing to the skin and has a wonderful tropical cocktail fragrance.

lant soothing clay healing her
aring leaf purifying seed calmin
eauty skin exfoliating relaxing nu
leansing flower moisture mask bu
alm petal gel refreshing massag
alt bath aromatherapy breathin
ruit wellness roots tincture vitamir
nfusion balance harmony honey fee
vash plant soothing clay healin
erb caring leaf purifying see
alming beauty skin exfoliatin
elaxing nut cleansing flowe
moisture mask bud balm petal ge
efreshing massage salt bat
romatherapy breathing fru
ellness roots tincture vitamir
nfusion balance bloom create spi

PERFUMES

- Fragrant Harmony
- Creating Perfumes

Fragrant Harmony

A natural perfume is a harmonious composition of pure essential oils — a symphony of top, middle and base notes. Creating a perfume has been described as being like composing music.

As soon as you open a bottle of perfume, you smell the top notes as they quickly escape from the bottle. They are the fresh, vibrant, lightweight ingredients which give you the initial impression of a fragrance. After applying your perfume to your skin, the top notes will diffuse for up to half an hour or so finally giving way to less diffusive middle notes, the heart of the perfume. The middle notes will release themselves over several hours after which all that remains are the base notes. These are the least diffusive notes of all. They are the heavy woody, resinous notes. They also function as fixatives as well, ensuring the top notes don't disappear too quickly. Dividing odours into categories of top, middle and base notes provides a means of classifying odours according to their volatility.

Professional perfumers may use hundreds of fragrance ingredients, both natural and synthetic, and many years to create a unique composition which smells exquisite at all stages as it releases itself from the skin.

When creating a perfume from pure essential oils it is important to consider the following points.

- Firstly, become familiar with the fragrance of each individual essential oil you have.

- Be aware of the various odour intensities of each essential oil. You will want to use less of an essential oil which has a strong, penetrating odour and more of an oil with a light, fresh odour.

- Choose essential oils from each classification of top, middle and base notes to create a pefume which unfolds harmoniously.

- Determine the kind of fragrance you want to achieve — fresh and citrusy, exotic and spicy, subtle and woody, sensual and floral, calming and soothing or whatever your heart desires. The essential oils that you choose can enhance or balance your mood.

The following proportions give you an indication of the quantity of the essential oil to be used in each note of a perfume blend. However, this will vary according to the notes you wish to have the most impact.

- 45-55% top notes

- 30-40% middle notes

- 15-25% base notes

The essential oils have been categorised into top, middle and base notes to assist you in your blending. Some essential oils will cross over into another category depending on the other essential oils used in your blend. Thus, these categories are only arbitrary.

Top notes

Basil	Lime
Bergamot	Mandarin
Citronella	Neroli
Grapefruit	Orange
Lemon	Tangerine
Lemongrass	

Middle notes

Black pepper	Marjoram
Cinnamon	Palmarosa
Clary sage	Petitgrain
Clove	Pine
Eucalyptus	Rose
Frankincense	Rosemary
Geranium	Rosewood
Ginger	Tea tree
Jasmine	Thyme
Juniper	Ylang ylang
Lavender	

Base notes

Cedarwood, Atlas	Patchouli
Cedarwood, Virginian	Sandalwood
Chamomile, German	Vetiver
Myrrh	

Pure perfume essential oil compositions

The pure perfume essential oil compositions on the following page are balanced blends which may be added to any of the perfume bases to make a parfum, extrait, eau de parfum, eau de toilette, eau de cologne, body splash, body spray or perfume oil.

Of these, parfum has the highest concentration of essential oils, with the concentration falling until it quite low in a body splash. You would use only a small quantity of parfum, whereas you would use a body spray quite liberally.

The total quantity of essential oil in each composition listed on page 112 is equivalent to one per cent if added to 100ml of perfume base. This makes it easy to calculate the quantity of essential oil you will need to add to a perfume base to make your desired strength of perfume. If, for example, you would like to make 100ml of eau de toilette, just multiply the quantity of drops by ten to give you a ten per cent dilution.

Personal Fragrance	Essential Oil	Alcohol/ Water
Parfum/Extrait	15-30%	Alcohol 90% Water 10%
Eau de Parfum	8-15%	Alcohol 85% Water 15%
Eau de Toilette	4-8%	Alcohol 80% Water 20%
Eau de Cologne/ Aftershave	3-5%	Alcohol 70% Water 30%
Body Splash/ Spray	1-3%	Alcohol 60% Water 40% or Essential oil solubiliser 2-6% Water 94-98%
Perfume Oil/ Balm	10-30%	Base oil or Balm

You may like to try one of the pure essential oil compositions on the following page before taking the next step of trusting your nose and your knowledge to make your own perfume composition.

Pure Perfume Essential Oil Compositions

Composition one

Spicy and Oriental
5 drops sweet orange
4 drops bergamot
3 drops cinnamon
2 drops lavender
3 drops Virginian cedarwood
3 drops patchouli

Composition two

Rich floral
6 drops rose absolute
6 drops geranium
3 drops frankincense
5 drops rosewood

Composition three

Green, herbaceous and lively
8 drops lemon
4 drops lemongrass
3 drops rosemary
3 drops petitgrain
2 drops ginger
2 drops vetiver

Composition four

Green and cool
4 drops lavender
4 drops geranium
5 drops spearmint
3 drops fennel
4 drops rosewood

Composition five

Warm and woody
6 drops mandarin
3 drops grapefruit
2 drops palmarosa
2 drops myrrh
7 drops sandalwood

Composition six

Floriental
4 drops bergamot
3 drops lime (distilled)
4 drops jasmine
2 drops ylang ylang
2 drops clove
3 drops Atlas cedarwood
2 drops patchouli

Composition seven

Traditional eau de cologne
3 drops neroli
1 drop petitgrain
4 drops orange
4 drops lemon
4 drops bergamot
2 drops rosemary
2 drops lavender

Compositions one, three, four, five and seven are also suitable for aftershaves.

Creating Perfumes

Creating a totally pure and natural perfume from essential oils satisfies both your nose and your soul. To make a perfume you will require a selection of essential oils and base ingredients to act as carriers.

Perfume Bases

There are several perfume base ingredients into which you can blend your essential oils. These include water, alcohol and oil. Pure essential oils are blended into these bases in various concentrations. This will then determine the strength of the perfume and consequently the way in which it is then used on the body.

Water

Distilled water is the water of choice. If this is not readily available to you, bottled spring or filtered water will suffice. Waters of distillation such as lavender water, rosewater or orange flower water may also be used where their fragrance complements the essential oils chosen. Essential oils do not readily disperse throughout water. If you add essential oils to water alone you need to shake your container each time you use your perfume. An essential oil dispersant or alcohol will ensure the essential oils stay dispersed throughout the water.

Alcohol

Alcohol is used as a perfume base for essential oils and assists in their evaporation and diffusion.

Perfume grade ethanol is the alcohol of choice. It is a fine grade alcohol made by the fermentation of starches, for example sugar. It is usually denatured to prevent its internal consumption.

As perfume grade ethanol is not available for purchase without an alcohol licence, some aromatherapy companies provide a perfume base which has had orris root or benzoin gum steeped in it. They act as fixatives for the perfume, helping the oils to remain on the skin longer. Vodka is a readily available substitute for the alcohol and water base for use in homemade perfumes.

Oil

Jojoba oil is the base oil of choice in making a perfume oil. It is relatively odorless and is very stable over a long period of time. Your next choice would be sweet almond oil or apricot kernel oil. They are not as stable as jojoba oil in the long term, but they are suitable if you are making small quantities which you intend to use within six months. They may also be a more economical choice.

Perfume balm

Pure essential oils may be added to a balm which you can store in a small pot. Make your perfume balm by following the directions for making an aromatherapy balm on page 30.

Making Your Perfume

This recipe is suitable for making an Eau de Toilette. Modify the quantities of ingredients according to the table on page 111 to make other types of perfumes.

80ml alcohol
20ml purified water
5ml essential oils of your choice

1. Blend your choice of pure essential oils.
2. Blend your essential oils with an equal quantity of alcohol.
3. Mix the water and remaining alcohol.
4. Slowly add the essential oil and alcohol mixture to the water and alcohol mixture, stirring as you go.
5. Store in a closed glass bottle for 24 hours in a cool place.
6. Filter the cooled perfume through filter paper.
7. Store in a sealed glass bottle to allow your perfume to develop to its full maturity for at least three months. Keep it in a cool place out of the light.
8. Your perfume is now ready for use.

This is a traditional method of making perfumes. It requires time and patience. However, if you so choose, your perfume may be used at anytime after you have blended it.

Aftershave

Follow the same procedure as above. However, at step 3 add some glycerin to the alcohol before adding it to the water. The glycerin will help reduce the drying effects the alcohol may have on the skin. Add approximately 5ml for each 100ml of aftershave.

The body spray method can be an alternative for making a gentle aftershave.

Body sprays

1. Blend your choice of pure essential oils.
2. Add essential oil dispersant to the essential oil blend.
3. Add the water to the essential oil and dispersant blend.
4. Shake the bottle.
5. It is now ready for use.

Perfume oils

1. Blend your choice of pure essential oils.
2. Add the base oil to the essential oil blend.
3. Shake the bottle.
4. Allow a day or two for the blend to mature if desired.
5. It is now ready for use.

Fresh from the Garden Perfumes

Beautiful eau de colognes, body splashes and aftershaves can be made from the fragrant herbs and flowers in your garden. They are simple to make and truly worth the effort.

Try any of these fragrant ingredients or others which you may have in your garden

Flowers   Frangipani, honeysuckle, jasmine, lavender, roses.

Herbs	Eucalyptus, geranium, lemon balm, lemon grass, lemon myrtle, lemon verbena, peppermint, rosemary, sage, thyme.
Citrus	Grapefruit, lemon, lime, mandarin, and orange peels.
Spices	Cinnamon, clove, ginger.

Ingredients

1 cup freshly crushed herbs or uncrushed flowers
1½ cups water
1 cup perfume base alcohol or vodka

To make your fragrant eau de cologne, body splash or aftershave follow either of the following two methods:

Maceration method

1. Macerate (steep) all ingredients together in a glass jar for two weeks.
2. Strain the mixture through muslin, squeezing out the last drops.
3. Pour into a bottle and store away from heat and light.
4. Allow to mature for a fortnight before using. (If you feel the perfume needs to be stronger, repeat the process with fresh flowers or herbs.)

Decoction method

1. Pour the water and flowers or herbs into a saucepan. Cover with a lid
2. Bring to boiling point.
3. Simmer gently for 30 minutes.
4. Allow to cool without removing the lid.
5. Strain the flowers or herbs from the fragrant water through muslin, squeezing out the last drops. If you feel the perfume needs to be stronger, repeat the process with the same water and fresh flowers or herbs.

6. Add the alcohol to the fragrant water.
7. Pour into a bottle and store away from heat and light.
8. Allow a fortnight for all ingredients to blend and mature.

Hungary water

This recipe is based on a traditional cologne first made in the 14th century and named after Queen Elizabeth of Hungary.

4 tbsp rosemary freshly crushed
3 tbsp mint freshly crushed
3 tbsp roses freshly crushed
1 tbsp grated lemon rind
100ml orange flower water
50ml purified water
150ml perfume base alcohol or vodka

Make this perfume using the maceration or decoction method.

Chilled cucumber body splash

1 cup juiced cucumber
2 cups vodka

1. Strain the cucumber.
2. Blend the cucumber juice with the vodka.
3. Store in the refrigerator for a chilled cucumber body splash to be used whenever you need refreshing.

plant soothing clay healing her
aring leaf purifying seed calmin
eauty skin exfoliating relaxing nu
leansing flower moisture mask bu
alm petal gel refreshing massag
alt bath aromatherapy breathin
ruit wellness roots tincture vitami
nfusion balance harmony honey fee
vash plant soothing clay healin
erb caring leaf purifying see
alming beauty skin exfoliatin
elaxing nut cleansing flowe
oisture mask bud balm petal ge
efreshing massage salt bat
romatherapy breathing fru
vellness roots tincture vitami
fusion balance bloom create spit

HAIR

- Hair and Scalp Ingredients

- Hair Shampoos

- Hair Conditioners

- Hair and Scalp Treatments

- Hair Styling

- Hair Colours

Hair and Scalp Ingredients

Understanding the active ingredients which are used to make your hair and scalp preparations will allow you to create many new preparations and adapt the ones given here to suit your own needs.

Pure essential oils

Pure essential oils have many properties which benefit the hair and scalp. They are most therapeutically beneficial when massaged into the scalp where they benefit the health of the scalp and subsequently the health of the hair.

Essential oils may have a direct effect on the hair itself in that they are partially absorbed into the surface of the hair shaft along with any vegetable oils used in the preparation and the hair's own natural sebum (oil). The effects of the essential oils in this instance would probably extend only as far as adding some shine to the hair. Most benefit is derived from the essential oils being absorbed and utilised by the scalp. Do not choose essential oils according to your hair colour as they do not affect hair colour.

- **Rosemary, ginger** and **pine** stimulate the circulation in the scalp which in turn improves blood flow to the hair papillae and follicles where hair growth takes place. Use these oils when poor hair growth is a problem.

- **Sandalwood** and **rosewood** improve dry hair and scalp conditions.

- **Bergamot, cedarwood, cypress, geranium, grapefruit, lemon** and **patchouli** help balance an excessively oily hair and scalp condition.

- **Lavender** and **chamomile,** due to their anti-inflammatory properties, may be used on inflamed, irritated scalps and are gentle enough to use on babies' scalps as well.

- **Cajeput, cedarwood, eucalyptus, peppermint, rosemary, spike lavender, tea tree,** and **thyme** will help clear dandruff conditions.

- **Lavender, rosemary** and **ylang ylang** may be used on most hair and scalp types as general tonics.

The pure essential oil compositions on the following page may be added to the following preparations:

- **Shampoos.** Add 20 drops of pure essential oil or pure essential oil composition to 100 ml of liquid Castile soap or shampoo base.

- **Hair and scalp treatment oils.** Add up to 50 drops of pure essential oil or pure essential oil composition to each 100 ml of cold-pressed vegetable oil.

- **Hair conditioning preparations.** Add 20 drops of pure essential oil, or pure essential oil composition, to each 100 ml of your conditioning recipes which you will learn to make on page 125.

- **Hair vinegars and rinses.** Add five drops of pure essential oil, or a pure essential oil composition, to each 500 ml of the rinse recipes, which you will learn to make on page 120.

Infused oils

Infused oils such as carrot and calendula are beneficial for scalp problems.

Carrot infused oil is beneficial in alleviating dry, flaky scalp conditions.

Calendula infused oil is beneficial in alleviating irritated scalp conditions.

Infused oils may be applied to your scalp directly or blended with cold-pressed vegetable oils. Essential oils may be combined with the infused oils for a scalp treatment.

You may like to use these essential oil compositions in your hair care preparations.

Pure Essential Oil Compositions

Oily hair composition
Balances oiliness
8 drops lemon
4 drops cypress
4 drops geranium
4 drops lavender

Dry hair composition
Improves shine and condition
10 drops sandalwood
4 drops ylang ylang
6 drops lavender

All hair types composition
A general hair and scalp tonic
5 drops rosemary
8 drops lavender
7 drops geranium

Inflamed, irritated scalp conditions
Anti-inflammatory and soothing
3 drops blue chamomile
7 drops lavender
5 drops rosewood

Baby's hair composition
Gentle and soothing
2 drops blue or Roman chamomile
3 drops lavender

Dandruff and itchy scalps composition
Relieves dry, flaky scalps
6 drops rosemary
7 drops cedarwood
7 drops spike lavender

Psoriasis of the scalp composition
Helps relieve this scalp condition
5 drops bergamot
4 drops juniper
5 drops blue chamomile
6 drops lavender

Hair loss composition
Stimulates scalp circulation
6 drops rosemary
7 drops ginger
7 drops spike lavender

Cold-pressed vegetable oils

Cold-pressed vegetable oils lubricate and protect the hair improving its shine and lustre. They are also used as scalp treatments to improve the condition of the scalp.

Coconut oil is traditionally used as a hair and scalp treatment in the Pacific Islands, olive oil is used in Mediterranean countries, and jojoba oil was used by Native Americans. Sweet almond oil and apricot kernel oil are suitable hair and scalp oils.

Fruits and vegetables

Grapefruit and lemon

Grapefruit juice and lemon juice which have been strained may be used in preparations for oily hair.

Avocado

Avocado is rich in conditioning oil. Ripe avocado flesh mashed into a smooth creamy paste makes a wonderful hair conditioner.

Eggs

Eggs are used to soften and smooth your hair. The yolk is best used for dry hair and the white for oily hair.

Henna

Henna is a herb which coats the hair shaft giving it a lustrous shine. It is available in a variety of colours or in clear/neutral if you do not wish to add colour to your hair.

Herbs

Herbal extracts, including infusions, vinegars and oils, are wonderful preparations to use to improve the condition of your hair and scalp.

Herbal infusions

Herbal infusions may be used as final hair rinses to add shine to your hair and to improve the health of your scalp. Make a herbal infusion by following the instructions on page 24.

After shampooing and conditioning your hair, pour the infusion over your scalp and throughout your hair. There is no need to rinse it out; it leaves a gorgeous subtle fragrance in your hair, depending on the herb.

Herbal infusions may also be added to your shampoos.

Herbal infusions can be used to add subtle coloured highlights to your hair. For more information see the section on herbal hair colours on page 131.

Herbal vinegars

Herbal vinegars may be used to improve the condition of your scalp especially if you have a problem with dandruff. The herbal vinegars not only re-establish the acid pH of your scalp and hair but also include the beneficial therapeutic properties of the herbs in the vinegar. Herbal vinegars may be used regularly after shampooing and conditioning. They also help minimise the build-up of hair products in the hair.

Follow the instructions for making a herbal vinegar which you learned to make on page 26.

Add 20ml (1 tbsp) of your herbal vinegar to one litre of water and massage into your scalp and pour throughout your hair. You may want to follow with a quick rinse of warm water or herbal infusion.

For more detailed information on each of the individual herbs see page 8.

Herbal oils

Herbal oils condition your hair and treat your scalp. They can also be beautifully fragrant depending on the herbs you choose to infuse into your base oil. Follow the instructions for making a herbal oil on page 25. Your herbal oils may be used in your shampoos and conditioners, especially if your hair is dry. However, they are best used as they are, as treatments for your hair and scalp. Essential oils may also be incorporated into your herbal oil preparations.

Hair Shampoos

Clean your hair with a pure plant shampoo and give yourself a stimulating scalp massage. This will leave you and your hair feeling clean and refreshed.

Making a shampoo base from the basic necessary ingredients is an uneconomical alternative as the ingredients are available only in large bulk quantities. This makes the purchasing of the individual ingredients prohibitive for the individual shampoo maker.

Plant-derived shampoo bases and liquid Castile soap are readily available and simplify the process of making shampoos.

If using liquid Castile soap, it is important to use a vinegar hair rinse regularly after shampooing to reduce alkaline effects and to minimise soap build up on the hair shaft.

Aromatherapy shampoo

20 drops essential oil
100ml liquid Castile soap or
shampoo base

1. Choose the appropriate essential oils or essential oil composition for your hair and scalp.

2. Add the essential oils to the liquid Castile soap or shampoo base and shake or stir thoroughly. If your hair is dry, add 10ml of cold pressed vegetable oil to the mixture.

3. Store in a clean bottle or container.

Herbal shampoo

25ml strong herbal infusion or decoction
75ml liquid Castile soap or
shampoo base
1ml citrus seed extract

1. Choose the appropriate herbs for your hair and scalp. If your hair is particularly oily, replace the herbal infusion or decoction totally or partially with strained and filtered grapefruit or lemon juice. If your hair is dry, add 10ml of cold pressed vegetable oil to the mixture.

2. Prepare a herbal infusion or decoction (page 24), strain and filter.

3. Add the citrus seed extract and the infusion or decoction to the liquid Castile soap or shampoo base and shake thoroughly.

4. Store in a clean bottle or container.

Soapwort hair cleanser

This is an excellent hair cleanser for sensitive or problem scalps as well as for fine or damaged hair. Soapwort root is high in saponins which, when released, produce a mild lather that will gently cleanse your hair and scalp.

20gm soapwort root
500ml water or herbal infusion

1. Make a herbal decoction using the procedure you learned on page 24.

2. Pour into an empty bottle or container and shake well.

3. Massage into damp hair and rinse thoroughly. Your hair will feel soft and clean.

4. Keep for only a couple of days.

Egg shampoos

A very simple method of cleansing your hair which leaves your hair soft and clean.

Dry hair egg shampoo

1 egg yolk
150ml warm water or herbal infusion

1. Whisk the egg yolk and then whisk the water into it.

2. Massage the mixture throughout your hair, leave in for a couple of minutes.

3. Rinse thoroughly with warm water. (Hot water will cook the egg onto your hair).

Oily hair egg shampoo

1 egg white
150ml warm water or herbal infusion

1. Whisk the egg white and then whisk the water into it.

2. Massage the mixture throughout your hair, and leave in for a couple of minutes.

3. Rinse thoroughly with warm water. (Hot water will cook the egg onto your hair).

Green clay herbal hair cleanser

This is a cleansing and normalising preparation for oily hair. It is also helpful if the oily hair is accompanied by a flaky, itchy scalp.

25gm green clay
75ml herbal infusion
1 tbsp (20ml) apple cider vinegar

1. Make an infusion by following the directions on page 24, using the herbs recommended for oily hair.

2. Add the herbal infusion and apple cider vinegar to the clay and mix into a smooth paste.

3. Apply to your scalp and massage in well then spread the remains of the mixture throughout the rest of your hair.

(If your scalp is oily and the ends of your hair are dry use the mixture on your scalp only.)

Green clay shampoo

25gm green clay
100ml shampoo base
20 drops essential oils for oily hair

1. Stir all ingredients together thoroughly.

2. Store in a clean bottle or container.

3. Use as you would a normal shampoo and massage into your hair and scalp. Rinse thoroughly with warm water. This shampoo won't lather like normal shampoo but will cleanse your hair.

Pure pulse shampoo

This is a very gentle cleansing preparation for fine, dry or damaged hair. It is made using finely milled dried peas, beans and pulses. You may choose to prepare them yourself or alternatively you can purchase them as flours. Chickpeas and lentils are both traditionally used ingredients. They absorb any dirt and grime from the hair which is then rinsed away.

50gm chickpea or lentil flour
400ml spring water or herbal infusion

1. Place the flour into a saucepan.
2. Slowly add the water or herbal infusion and mix into a smooth paste.
3. Gently heat the mixture for about 20 minutes.
4. Stir the mixture constantly to ensure it does not stick to the bottom of the saucepan.

or

1. Cook your lentils or chickpeas as per instructions on the packet.
2. Then put them into a blender or mash them into a smooth paste.
3. Massage the warm paste into your scalp and throughout your hair.
4. Rinse thoroughly from your hair.

Aromatic dry shampoo

This hair cleanser works by absorbing the oil and grime from your hair. It also leaves your hair smelling wonderfully aromatic. Use it whenever you don't want to or can't shampoo your hair with water.

25gm orris root powder
25gm semolina or cornstarch or cornmeal or rice flour or ground rice
10 drops essential oils of your choice

1. Massage small quantities into your hair close to your scalp then spread and massage the mixture throughout your hair.
2. Use a brush to distribute the mixture throughout your hair and to begin to remove it.
3. Remove the rest by tipping your head upside down and continuing to brush.

Oily hair toner

Whenever your scalp is particularly oily, apply pure witch hazel water or lavender water to a cotton wool ball or pad and wipe throughout your hair and over your scalp to remove the excess oil.

Hair Conditioners

While shampoos remove dirt and grime, they also lift the cuticle scales on the shaft of the hair and remove the hair's natural oils. Conditioning ensures that the cuticle scales are once again smoothed and the hair oils are somewhat replenished. This is particularly important for dry, damaged or brittle hair.

Amazing avocado conditioner

A softening conditioner for fine, dry hair. This recipe makes enough for one application.

½ ripe avocado
5ml (1 tsp) avocado oil
1 egg yolk

1. Mash the avocado flesh into a smooth paste.

2. Blend in the avocado oil and egg yolk.

3. After shampooing, spread the amazing avocado conditioner throughout your hair and leave on for a few minutes before rinsing.

4. Rinse thoroughly.

Ultra-rich hair conditioner

Slather this conditioner on your hair if it is dry and damaged. This recipe makes enough for one application.

2 egg yolks
20ml (1 tbsp) cold pressed vegetable oil
(coconut, olive or jojoba oil)
10ml (2 tsp) apple cider vinegar
10ml (2tsp) honey
10ml (2 tsp) lecithin

1. Mix all of the ingredients.

2. After shampooing, spread the ultra-rich conditioner throughout your hair and leave on for a few minutes before rinsing.

3. Rinse thoroughly.

Honey hair conditioner

A wonderful conditioner for normal to dry hair. It is also very good for your hair if it is fine and dry.

Oil phase

10gm plant-derived emulsifying wax
5ml (1 tsp) honey
30ml jojoba oil

Water phase

275ml purified water
20ml (1 tbsp) vegetable glycerin
2ml (½ tsp) citrus seed extract

Add at 45°C

50 drops essential oil or
all hair types composition (see page 119)

1. Make your honey hair conditioner by following the directions for making an emulsion on page 36.

2. Store in a clean container and use after each shampoo.

3. Spread your honey conditioner throughout your hair and leave on for a few minutes.

4. Rinse thoroughly.

Luscious lecithin hair conditioner

A fantastic hair conditioner for dry, damaged and brittle hair. It softens and shines your hair.

Oil phase

15ml coconut oil
20ml lecithin
5gm plant-derived emulsifying wax

Water phase

50ml purified water
30 drops citrus seed extract

Add at 45°C

10 drops essential oil or dry hair composition (see page 119)

1. Make your luscious lecithin conditioner by following the directions for making an emulsion on page 36.

2. Store your conditioner in a clean container and use after each shampoo.

3. Spread your luscious lecithin conditioner throughout your hair and leave on for a few minutes.

4. Rinse thoroughly.

Hair and Scalp Treatments

Improve the health of your hair and scalp by choosing to use a treatment preparation on a regular basis.

Hair and scalp treatment

1. Massage the treatment into your scalp. (It may be spread throughout your hair and used as a hair treatment too.)

2. Cover your hair and scalp with a shower cap or cling film and wrap in a warm towel to enhance to absorption of essential oils and active ingredients. This step is optional and may be unnecessary during the summer months.

3. Leave on for at least half an hour before shampooing your hair.

Hair and scalp treatment oils

Treatment oils are particularly beneficial for treating dry and damaged hair as well as scalp problems such as dandruff and dry, flaky scalps, inflamed and irritated scalps, psoriasis of the scalp and hair loss. They can also improve circulation in the scalp.

Head lice oil

This is a concentrated aromatherapy blend which can be used to eliminate head lice.

15 drops thyme essential oil
15 drops rosemary essential oil
20 drops geranium essential oil
50ml jojoba oil

1. Apply the treatment oil as you would a hair and scalp treatment and leave on for as long as possible.

2. Shampoo the hair.

3. As a final rinse, add two drops of each essential oil to 500ml of water and pour through the hair.

Dandruff treatment oil

An excellent aromatherapy oil for relieving the itching scalp and dry flakes of dandruff.

10 drops rosemary essential oil
10 drops spike lavender essential oil
10 drops cedarwood essential oil
50ml jojoba oil

1. Apply the treatment oil as you would a scalp treatment and leave on for at least half an hour before shampooing your hair. Use this treatment each time you wash your hair, then reduce it to once a week, then once a fortnight.

2. Follow with a vinegar rinse for dandruff or apple cider vinegar. Add one tablespoon of vinegar to one litre of water and pour over your scalp.

Hair loss treatment oil

Use this aromatherapy oil to encourage circulation to, and stimulation of, the hair follicle.

10 drops rosemary essential oil
10 drops ginger essential oil
10 drops peppermint essential oil
50ml jojoba oil

Apply the treatment oil as you would a scalp treatment and leave on for at least half an hour before shampooing your hair. While the oil is on, perform a gently stimulating massage on the scalp for a few minutes. Use this treatment once a week.

Cradle cap treatment oil

Sweet almond oil, apricot kernel oil and evening primrose oil, either used together or individually, may be massaged into your baby's scalp to help soften the build-up of the cradle cap. A drop of blue chamomile essential oil may be added to 50 ml of base oil to soothe the scalp.

Following the massage, shampoo with a mild shampoo and gently lift the scales by massaging the baby's scalp with a soft baby brush.

Hair conditioning treatments

We subject our hair to many damaging elements which strip the hair of its natural oil making it dry and brittle and prone to split ends.

Hair conditioners and treatments lubricate and protect our hair, improving its shine and lustre. They replace the natural oil which normally flows from the sebaceous glands of our scalp down the shaft of each hair as well as helping to smooth the cuticle scales of the hair shaft.

Henna conditioning treatment

100gm neutral/clear henna powder
500ml boiling water
20ml cold-pressed vegetable oil
(coconut, olive or jojoba oil)
1 egg yolk

1. Mix the henna powder, boiling water and cold pressed oil together in a bowl.
2. Once the mixture has cooled a little, add the egg yolk.
3. Apply the mixture to your hair by following the instructions for using a hair and scalp treatment on page 127.

Lecithin conditioning treatment

5ml liquid lecithin
40ml cold-pressed vegetable oil
(coconut, olive or jojoba oil)
5gm cocoa butter

1. Melt all ingredients together in a bain-marie.
2. Once melted, pour the mixture into a clean container and use as required.
3. Apply the mixture to your hair by following the instructions for using a hair and scalp treatment on page 127.

Essential hair balm

A wonderful preparation for glossing thick, dry hair.

85gm cold-pressed vegetable oil
(coconut, olive or jojoba oil)
5gm beeswax
10gm cocoa butter
20 drops essential oils of your choice

1. Melt the beeswax, cocoa butter and vegetable oil in a bain-marie until the

beeswax and cocoa butter have both melted.

2. Once the mixture cools a little, add the essential oils.

3. Pour into a clean jar or pot to store.

4. Using a tiny amount on the tips of your fingers, spread the hair balm over your hair. Then using the palms of your hands smooth it throughout your hair. You may choose to use it on your dry ends only.

Hair Styling

Slick your hair back and keep it in place with a natural hair spray or give it volume and style with a natural hair gel. These natural styling products do not have quite as strong holding properties as commercial products.

Hair spray

A gentle hair spray for holding those stray hairs into place.

20gm sugar
80ml water or strained lemon juice

1. Dissolve the sugar into the water or lemon juice.

2. Pour into a spray bottle.

3. Your hair spray is now ready for use.

Hair gel

Slick your hair into place with this one. Made entirely from plants this gel contains no alcohol or plastic polymers.

100ml purified water
4gm xanthan gum
10 drops essential oils of your choice

1. Make the hair gel by following the instructions for making gels on page 31.

2. Add your choice of essential oils and mix in thoroughly.

3. Store your hair gel in a suitable clean container in the fridge.

Intensive hair cleanser

When your hair is slicked into place and sculpted into fabulous styles, a build-up is created on your hair with the products, which help your hair to stay in place. Once a week or once a fortnight use this formula to dissolve and remove any residues.

½ cup baking soda
1 cup warm water

1. Dissolve the baking soda into the warm water.

2. Pour over your hair and massage it into your hair.

3. Rinse well.

Hair Colours

You can enhance your own natural hair colour using herbs or change it dramatically by using henna which is also produced from a plant.

Herbal hair colours

Herbal hair colours are generally subtle, require several and regular applications and encourage healthier, shinier hair.

Choose from the following list of herbs to enhance your natural hair colour:

- Golden highlights — calendula petals, turmeric, rhubarb root.
- Fair highlights — chamomile flowers, lemon juice.
- Brown — espresso coffee, sage, strong black tea, walnut husks.

1. Make a strong decoction of your chosen herb or herbs and include one teaspoon of apple cider vinegar. Follow the instructions for making a decoction on page 24.
2. Simmer until the colour is strong.
3. Strain the herbs from the water.
4. Massage the warm decoction thoroughly throughout clean hair.
5. Cover your hair with plastic and leave on for at least one hour.
6. Rinse thoroughly with lukewarm water.

Henna

The use of henna and other herbs as hair colouring agents and conditioners has a long history. Henna is an excellent conditioner for the hair. It protects the ends from splitting and gives a glorious shine. It colours the hair, giving various colours and shades depending on the henna used and the original colour of your hair.

Henna was used extensively in ancient Egypt; Cleopatra and Nefertiti are reputed to have enhanced their beauty with it. Many Middle Eastern and Indian women and men continue to use it today, not only to dye their hair, but to colour their fingernails and to decorate their hands and bodies with intricate henna tattoos. Henna has also been shown to have antiseptic properties. Hence its traditional use on the soles of the feet as a form of protection.

It is made from the pulverised leaves of the henna plant (*Lawsonia* species) which is widely distributed throughout the tropics. In 1709, botanist and traveller, Dr Lawson, isolated the active ingredient in henna, lawsone, which is responsible for both its colouring and conditioning properties.

Henna varies a great deal in its lawsone content and thus its quality. Hot regions of the world yield the best henna which include countries such as Egypt, Iran, Pakistan and India. However, there are variations of quality produced within each of these countries. Poor quality henna is cheap and coarse, with little or no colouring ability because of the absence of lawsone. The consistency of poor quality henna when mixed with water is very gritty and not smooth. It is difficult to apply. Whereas good quality henna mixes with water into a smooth mud consistency. It is still messy to apply but is applied more easily.

Pure henna ranges in colour from red to orange to orange/yellow. Various herbs and spices are mixed with the pulverised henna powder to produce other colour variations. Indigo (*Indigo tinctoria*) and Woad (*Isatis tinctoria*) are used to produce black henna. Popular henna colours include red, auburn, chestnut, mahogany, burgundy, golden brown, brown, black and clear. Clear henna is used as a conditioning treatment without colouring the hair.

Precautions

Because the colouring outcome is more difficult to predict with henna than synthetic colours, it is essential to do a strand test first to help gauge the final colour outcome. Mix approximately a teaspoonful of the henna herbal hair colour with a small amount of boiling water and mix into a paste. Apply the henna to a small section of your hair, wrap in foil and, after the recommended period of time, rinse your hair and check the colour. This will help you decide whether it is appropriate for you.

The ultimate colour of your hair depends on your original hair colour and this will vary from person to person.

On bleached hair, the red-based hennas will take very strongly and the colour will be very bright. Brown and black henna colours will throw green tones on bleached hair.

Brown and black henna are best used on medium to dark shades of hair.

Henna does not take as well to grey hair, several applications may be required to build up initial depth of colour. As grey hair is lighter in colour, the red-based colours will initially tend to be lighter and brighter.

The use of henna is not recommended if you intend to have your hair permed in the near future. Henna does not allow the perming solution to penetrate the hair shaft properly.

Henna may be used over coloured hair as long as it has been several months since the colour was applied. A strand test must be carried out to check the colour interaction.

Applying henna to the hair

To make your henna hair colour you will require the following items and ingredients:

- plastic or rubber gloves;
- ceramic, glass or metal bowl;
- wooden, metal or plastic mixing spoon;
- newspaper to cover the floor and table;
- old towel;
- old clothes to wear;
- plastic shower cap, cling film or plastic grocery bag;
- Henna (100gm is enough to cover hair a little longer than shoulder-length);
- boiling water;
- vinegar;
- egg;
- vegetable oil.

1. Set aside several hours to henna your hair and to allow the colour to develop. Read a good book, watch a good video or two, or do the housework while you're waiting for the colour to develop.

2. Cover your table and floor around you with newspaper, prepare your utensils, and put on your old clothes.

3. Apply vegetable oil to the skin around your hair line to prevent it from being stained.

4. Mix the henna powder with enough boiling water to give it the consistency of a cake batter. (Water may be replaced with wine, beetroot juice, tea or strong coffee to vary the shade of the henna. You can replace the water completely as the liquid component, but the liquid should be hot.) Add a good dash of vinegar to the mixture to create an acid environment that will enhance colour development.

Mix an egg throughout the mixture so that it sticks to the hair better and gives it extra conditioning properties.

If your hair is particularly dry, add a tablespoon of cold pressed vegetable oil to the mixture.

5. Apply the mixture with a tint brush or gloved fingers to clean dry hair. Apply to small sections at a time, starting from the roots. Work from the underneath layers to the top layers. Lastly, do the ends, as these, in long hair, are often both lighter in colour and more porous, taking the colour faster.

6. Make sure your hair is evenly coated. Leave the mixture on your hair to dry. This may be assisted gently with a hair dryer. Otherwise, cover your hair with plastic (such as a plastic shower cap, cling film or shopping bag).

7. Leave the colours on for the following lengths of time.

    Red: . . . . up to 1 hour
    Auburn: . . . . up to 3 hours
    Chestnut: . . . . 1 to 5 hours
    Mahogany: . . . 2 hours
    Burgundy: . . . 2-6 hours
    Golden Brown: . up to 1 hour

    Brown: . . . . . 4-6 hours
    Black: . . . . . 4-6 hours

8. Rinse the henna thoroughly from your hair. This could take a while if your hair is long. Then shampoo and condition.

In general, henna fades gently from your hair over two to three months. However, if your hair is dry and porous it will last a lot longer and could be a permanent colour. It is also possible to create shade variations by mixing the various henna powders together.

plant soothing clay healing her
aring leaf purifying seed calmin
eauty skin exfoliating relaxing nu
leansing flower moisture mask bu
alm petal gel refreshing massag
alt bath aromatherapy breathin
uit wellness roots tincture vitamin
fusion balance harmony honey fee
ash plant soothing clay healin
erb caring leaf purifying see
alming beauty skin exfoliatin
elaxing nut cleansing flowe
oisture mask bud balm petal ge
efreshing massage salt bat
romatherapy breathing fru
ellness roots tincture vitamin
fusion balance bloom create spic

USEFUL
INFORMATION

- Skin Care Guide to Herbs and Essential Oils

- Hair Care Guide to Herbs and Essential Oils

- Glossary

- Further Reading

- List of Recipes

- Index

Skin Care Guide to Herbs and Essential Oils

Skin type or condition	Essential oils	Herbs
All skin types	Jasmine, lavender, neroli, rose	Aloe vera, calendula, chamomile, comfrey, lavender, soapwort
Oily	Bergamot, cypress, geranium, juniper, lemon, lime, mandarin, orange, tangerine	Aloe vera, lavender, witch hazel, yarrow
Combination	Geranium, lavender, palmarosa, ylang ylang	Aloe vera, elderflowers
Dry	Palmarosa, rose, rosewood, sandalwood	Aloe vera, comfrey root, marshmallow root, rose, slippery elm
Mature	Carrot seed, fennel, frankincense, lavender, myrrh, patchouli, rose, rosewood, sandalwood	Ginseng, gota kola, green tea, rose
Dehydrated	Palmarosa, rose, rosewood, sandalwood	Aloe vera, comfrey root, marshmallow root, rose, slippery elm
Sensitive	Blue chamomile, everlasting, jasmine, lavender, neroli, rose, rosewood, sandalwood, yarrow	Aloe vera, calendula, chamomile, comfrey, gotu kola, green tea, liquorice, marshmallow, soapwort
Acne	Bergamot, cedarwood, chamomile (blue and Roman), clary sage, cypress, eucalyptus, everlasting, geranium, grapefruit, juniper, lavender, lemon, may chang, myrrh, palmarosa, patchouli, petitigrain, pine, tea tree, thyme, yarrow	Aloe vera, calendula, comfrey, garlic, gotu kola, lemon balm, lemongrass, sage, thyme, yarrow

Skin type or condition	Essential oils	Herbs
Devitalised	Grapefruit, lemongrass, peppermint, rosemary, vetiver	Lemongrass, nettle, rosemary
Boils	Myrrh, tea tree, thyme	Fenugreek, marshmallow, myrrh, slippery elm
Broken capillaries	Blue chamomile, cypress, geranium, lemon	Gotu kola
Bruises	Black pepper, lavender, spike lavender	Arnica, comfrey, hypericum, witch-hazel
Burns	Lavender, chamomile (blue and Roman)	Aloe vera, calendula, chamomile
Herpes simplex (cold sores)	Bergamot, melissa, myrrh, tea tree, thyme	Lemon balm, myrrh
Cracked skin	Myrrh, patchouli, sandalwood	Aloe vera, calendula, comfrey, marshmallow
Dermatitis/ Eczema	Blue chamomile, everlasting, lavender, myrrh, sandalwood, yarrow	Aloe vera, calendula, chamomile, chickweed, comfrey, liquorice root, marshmallow root
Deodorant	Bergamot, cedarwood, clary sage, cypress, eucalyptus, frankincense, geranium, juniper, lavender, patchouli, pine, rosewood, sandalwood, tea tree, ylang ylang	Lemon balm, lemongrass, peppermint, rosemary, sage, thyme
Tinea	Myrrh, tea tree, thyme	Calendula, garlic, myrrh, thuja
Mosquito bites	Lavender, peppermint, tea tree	Aloe vera, chamomile, calendula, peppermint

Skin type or condition	Essential oils	Herbs
Insect repellent	Cajeput, citronella, eucalyptus, geranium, lavender, lemongrass, peppermint, rosemary, spike lavender, tea tree, Virginian cedarwood	Lavender, pennyroyal
Pruritis, urticaria (itching, rashes)	Blue chamomile, lavender, peppermint, tea tree	Aloe vera, calendula, chamomile, chickweed, lavender, liquorice root, marshmallow root, peppermint
Psoriasis	Bergamot, blue chamomile, carrot seed, everlasting, juniper, lavender, sandalwood, yarrow	Aloe vera, calendula, chamomile, chickweed, comfrey, liquorice root, marshmallow root
Scarring	Blue chamomile, frankincense, lavender, myrrh, patchouli, rosewood	Aloe vera, calendula, comfrey, gotu kola
Verruca (warts)	Cinnamon leaf or bark, lemon, tea tree, thyme	Thuja
Wounds, cuts, sores	Bergamot, blue and Roman chamomile, everlasting, frankincense, geranium, lavender, myrrh, patchouli, tea tree, yarrow	Aloe vera, calendula, comfrey, fenugreek, myrrh, thyme, yarrow

Hair Care Guide to Herbs and Essential Oils

Hair type or scalp condition	Essential oils	Herbs
All hair types	Geranium, lavender, rosemary, ylang ylang	Henna, horsetail, lavender, rosemary, sage
Dry hair and damaged hair	Frankincense, rosewood, sandalwood	Aloe vera, chamomile, comfrey, marshmallow root, soap wort
Oily hair	Bergamot, cedarwood, cypress, geranium, grapefruit, juniper, lemon, lime, patchouli, petitgrain	Nettle, peppermint, thyme, yarrow
Baby and fine hair	Chamomile (blue and Roman), lavender	Calendula, chamomile, lavender
Dandruff	Cedarwood, cajeput, eucalyptus, spike lavender, rosemary, tea tree, thyme	Lavender, nettle, parsley, peppermint, rosemary, sage, thyme
Inflamed, irritated scalps (eczema and psoriasis)	Blue chamomile, lavender, sandalwood	Calendula, chamomile, comfrey, lavender, licorice, marshmallow, soapwort
Hair loss	Ginger, peppermint, rosemary, ylang ylang	Bay, ginger, nettle, peppermint, rosemary
Lice	Cinnamon, geranium, tea tree, thyme	

Glossary

Acid

Substance with a pH less than 7. Strong acids can be highly irritant.

Alkali

Substances with a pH above 7. Strongly alkaline substances are corrosive.

Allergen

Any substance that causes manifestations of allergy.

Allergy

An acquired hypersensitivity to a substance. A skin allergy may manifest as an unpleasant, red irritation which may become swollen, blistered or , in severe cases, develop into an open, flaking form of eczema. There may be a genetic predisposition to acquire a particular allergy. An allergy may occur within the first couple of times a person is exposed to a substance or may occur for the first time after years of repeated exposure.

Antibacterial

Inhibits the growth and reproduction of bacteria.

Anti-inflammatory

Reduces inflammation.

Anti-oxidant

Prevents the formation of free radicals, which can cause the oxidative deterioration that causes rancidity in oils or fats and premature aging. Vitamins A,C, and E are examples of anti-oxidants.

Antiperspirant

Substances or products which inhibit or prevent perspiration.

Antiseptic

Causes the prevention of sepsis by preventing or inhibiting the growth of causative micro-organisms.

Astringent

Causes the contraction of skin tissue.

Deodorant

Masks the odour produced by the action of our bacteria on perspiration.

Detergent

May be derived from petroleum or vegetable oil. A chemical which is used as a cleansing agent with foaming properties.

Disinfectant

Kills bacteria.

Emollient

Fatty or oily substance with a lubricating action that makes the skin feel softer and more pliable. Emollients reduce moisture loss from the skin.

Exfoliation

The removal of the surface layer of dead cells from the skin

Fixative

A substance that helps to slow the rate of evaporation of components of perfume formulations. It helps the perfume to last longer on the skin.

Humectant

Humectants have the ability to bind moisture. Often used in moisturizing preparations. Glycerin and honey are examples of humectants.

Inflammation

The reaction of tissue to injury. Symptoms include pain, heat, redness and swelling.

Natural

This term generally refers to substances which exist in nature and are not further processed. Plant-derived or modified plant substance are other terms which may be applied to substances which were originally from plants but have been treated, altered or modified in some way. The term natural has been widely abused in the cosmetics industry. A product may contain one or two substances of plant origin among many synthetic ingredients and yet be successfully marketed as natural.

Organic

An adjective used to desribe produce which has been grown without the use of artificial fertilizers or pesticides. In chemistry terminology it means a substance which contains carbon atoms.

pH

Refers to the level of acidity or alkalinity of a given substance. The hydrogen in a substance determines the substance's level of acidity or alkalinity. The pH of acidic substances ranges from 0 to 6.9 and of alkaline substances between 7.1 and 14. A pH of 7 is considered neutral. The normal pH of the skin ranges from around 5.5 to 6.5.

Solvent

A substance which is used to extract components from a plant and bring it into solution.

Surfactant

A shortened term for surface active agent. A substance with the ability to reduce the surface tension at the interface between two unlike surfaces. Soaps and detergents are examples of surfactants as they cause the suspension of dirt and oil in water so that they can be rinsed away.

Further Reading

Advanced Professional Skin Care, Peter T. Pugliese, M.D., APSC Publishing, USA, 1991

For information on the anatomy and physiology of the skin and the pathology and diagnosis of skin disorders. It also covers treatment of the skin as it relates to beauty therapists.

Aromatherapy Soap Making, Elizabeth Wright, Print Wright Australia, 1996.

This book contains easy to follow recipes on how to make your own vegetable soaps using natural ingredients. An excellent book for those of you who have never made soap before, and would like to make your own soap from scratch.

Bodycraft, Nerys Purchon, Hodder and Stoughton Pty Ltd, Australia, 1993.

This book contains recipes for natural skin and hair preparations. It also briefly discusses aromatherapy, nutrition and taking time out.

The Complete Guide to Aromatherapy, Salvatore Battaglia, The Perfect Potion, Australia, 1995.

The most comprehensive book on the subject of aromatherapy and its various applications.

The Herbal Medicine-Maker's Handbook. An Art and Science of Herbal Medicine-Making as taught at the California School of Herbal Studies, James Green, Herbalist.

An interesting book offering various methods and detailed information on making herbal preparations.

The Complete Soapmaker, Norma Coney, Sterling Publishing Co. Inc., USA, 1996.

Contains many beautiful photographs and recipes for soaps. An excellent book for those of you wanting to expand your soap-making horizons.

Jeanne Rose's Herbal Body Book, Jeanne Rose, The Putnam Publishing Group, USA, 1976.

A kitchen cosmetics book containing information on making many preparations using a wide array of unusual ingredients.

Make Your Own Cosmetics, Neal's Yard Remedies, Aurum Press Ltd, UK, 1997.

Contains many simple recipes made from readily available ingredients which you can prepare at home. It also contains an excellent section discussing ingredients found in many commercially available products.

Skin Care and Cosmetic Ingredients Dictionary, Natalia Michalun with M Varinia Michalun, Milady Publishing Company, USA, 1994.

This book discusses many of the ingredients, including natural, which are contained in today's cosmetics. It also discusses the anatomy and physiology of the skin as well as skin care.

List of Recipes

Main Index

Foot scrubs 98
Foot treatments 100
Frankincense 21
Fruits 4
Fuller's earth 13

G

Galen 43
Gel masks 31,59
Gel moisturisers 31
Gels 31
Geranium 21
Ginseng 9
Glycerin 13
Glycerin soaps 76
Gotu kola 9
Grains 6
Grapes 4
Green clay 11
Guar gum 13

H

Hair 118
Hair colours 131
Hair conditioners 125
Hair gels 31
Hair loss 128
Hair removal 91
Hair rinses 27
Hair shampoos 122
Hair styling 130
Hands 95
Head lice 127
Henna 132
Herbal balms 29
Herbal baths 102

Herbal decoctions 24
Herbal extracts 27
Herbal infused oils 25
Herbal infusions 24,46
Herbal massage oils 85
Herbal ointments 29
Herbal syrups 25
Herbal tinctures 25
Herbal vinegars 26,46
Herbs 8
High blood pressure 20
Honey 13,107
Hygiene 3
Hypericum oil 16

I

Infused Oils 15
Ingredients, raw 4
Insect repellents 90

J

Jasmine 21
Jojoba oil 7

K

Kaolin 13

L

Lanolin 13
Lavender 21
Lavender water 16
Lecithin 14,34
Lemon 4,21
Lemon balm 9
Lemongrass 9
Lettuce 4